Competition and Planning in the National Health Service

For Anne

Competition and Planning in the National Health Service

The danger of unplanned markets

Calum Paton

Senior Lecturer, University of Keele

CHAPMAN & HALL

London · Glasgow · Weinheim · New York · Tokyo · Melbourne · Madras

Published by Chapman & Hall, 2-6 Boundary Row, London SE1 8HN

Chapman & Hall, 2-6 Boundary Row, London SE1 8HN, UK

Blackie Academic & Professional, Wester Cleddens Road, Bishopbriggs, Glasgow G64 2NZ, UK

Chapman & Hall GmbH, Pappelallee 3, 69469 Weinheim, Germany

Chapman & Hall USA, One Penn Plaza, 41st Floor, New York, NY10119, USA

Chapman & Hall Japan, ITP - Japan, Kyowa Building, 3F, 2-2-1 Hirakawacho, Chiyoda-ku, Tokyo 102, Japan

Chapman & Hall Australia, Thomas Nelson Australia, 102 Dodds Street, South Melbourne, Victoria 3205, Australia

Chapman & Hall India, R. Seshadri, 32 Second Main Road, CIT East, Madras 600 035, India

Distributed in the USA and Canada by Singular Publishing Group, Inc., 4284 41st Street, San Diego, California 92105

First edition 1992
Reprinted 1995

Typeset in 10/12pt Palatino by Mews Photosetting, Beckenham, Kent
Printed in Great Britain by Athenaeum Press Ltd, Gateshead, Tyne & Wear

ISBN 0 412 47060 8

A Catalogue record for this book is available from the British Library

∞ Printed on acid-free paper, manufactured in accordance with ANSI/NISO Z39.48-1992 and ANSI/NISO Z39.48-1984 (Permanence of Paper)

28·6·95

Contents

Acknowledgements

The author is grateful to Longman for their permission to draw on his article 'The Prime Minister's Review of the National Health Service and the White Paper, *Working for Patients*', in *Social Policy Review 1989–90* (eds Nick Manning and Clare Ungerson), Longman (1990) for Chapters 3 and 6; to the editor of the *British Medical Journal* for permission to draw on 'The Health Service and the General Election', *British Medical Journal* (August 19, 1991), **303**, pp. 405–7, for Chapter 7.

Preface

This book discusses recent health policy in Britain, from the (then) Prime Minister's Review of the NHS and the subsequent White Paper *Working for Patients* (February 1989), to the effect upon health services. The aim is to consider different approaches to delivering health care – in particular, those of competition on the one hand, and planning on the other hand.

The Conservative government's plans for the future of the NHS from 1988 onwards were very confusing. This reflects the reliance of policy makers upon superficial imports of pro-competitive ideas into the health arena; conflicts between pragmatists and ideological zealots in the Conservative Party; and a cycle of attitudes and policy back and forth between radicalism and incrementalism in an astonishingly short time. Not only did the Review swing from radicalism to pragmatism and back: the implementation of the subsquent legislation suffered from a similar chronic schizophrenia.

On the one hand, introducing the market into health care may imply privatization; on the other hand, preserving public financing of the NHS and largely public ownership of health facilities can still permit market forces to operate through the so-called internal market. The scope and limitations of this doctrine are explored. The political context of health policy following the White Paper *Working for Patients* was likely to ensure that the negative effects of markets, without many of the positive, were achieved. Misunderstanding of foreign health care systems' lessons, and a failure to distinguish different types of planning have not helped. The types of public planning from which the NHS can benefit are discussed.

The book outlines the key features of the NHS and the problems which created the political controversy of the late 1980s. It then discusses the evolution of policy to the present day in order to highlight differing ideas on how to run the NHS and how to analyse them. I believe that the NHS is an admirable institution, warts and all, and that its survival after three terms of Margaret Thatcher and the uncertain Major administration is testimony to its strength as well as to its appeal. Nevertheless, problems still exist, and the danger of their being exacerbated by trends in policy established from 1988 to 1991 is still large and could reduce the stability and popularity of the NHS.

Throughout, the spotlight is on the question of the best means to preserve, improve, and extend the equitable delivery of health care. Conceptual analysis is linked with practical examination of current health policy, and rigour is combined with polemic. Overall, the emphasis is upon both theory and practice; both ideology and detail. Finally, the book outlines the ethical and political considerations in establishing priorities in health care.

I would like to thank in particular Shirley Fone for preparing the manuscript. Naturally, the variety of stimulating conversations I have had with doctors, managers, and my students (not mutually exclusive categories) means it would be churlish not to thank all those from whose insight I have benefited.

Calum R. Paton

Introduction: financing and providing health care

FINANCING HEALTH CARE

In theoretical terms, there are a number of alternative systems for financing health care, ranging from purely private financing to full public financing. Private financing normally implies that health care is supplied according to demand, rather than to any publicly defined notion of populations' needs. Public financing allows ethical and social definitions of equity in providing opportunity for access to health care by populations, groups, and social classes.

A continuum of types of financing must take account of the fact that the public $v.$ private distinction can be extended to include the notion of who is the purchaser. Is publicly raised money for a health service allocated to health authorities, individuals, or other purchasers? Is private money used directly by consumers, through third party insurance, or by buying subscriptions in a Health Maintenance Organization (HMO) which is responsible for both insuring the patient and providing care as needed?

Thus, the range of options can include:

- private purchase of health care directly by individuals;
- private purchase of health insurance;
- private subscription in HMOs;
- national, or group-based, health insurance (NHI) whereby regulation determines who is covered and who contributes to premiums, e.g. government; employers; and individuals;
- social-security-based insurance (may be a particular case of NHI);
- community self-help including income–generation to supplement other systems;
- local taxation-based public funding;
- public financing through an 'Earmarked' health tax;
- public financing through general taxation or general revenues, with funds going to health authorities which provide care;
- public financing, with funds going to purchasing health authorities, which buy care from alternative providers;

- public financing, with funds going to individuals in the form of vouchers;
- public financing, with funds going to GPs, health management units or other 'health maintenance organization'-type purchasers, which buy care on behalf of consumers.

PROVIDING HEALTH CARE

Theoretical alternatives for providing care vary from private, non-competitive systems, such as in the US prior to the 1960s, through private competitive systems, to public systems of varying degrees of central control. Perfect competition does not exist, in that health care markets show impediments to effective competition both on the provision (supply) side and on the purchasing (demand) side, more than typical markets in goods and services.

LEVELS OF EXPENDITURE

Third-party insurance, whether nationally regulated and available or not, encourages a higher supply of care as private providers can make profits (or surpluses, if non-profit) by selling to consumers who do not pay directly. Thus, for Britain, if it is desired to spend more on health care, changing to national health insurance could be one route; but increased outputs in supply of care (or outcomes in terms of better health) may not be proportionate to expenditure.

If Britain seeks to equal or approach France and Germany in terms of money spent on health care, – as gauged by % of GDP, or even per capita in real terms – doing it by more public financing could produce more output, with more efficiency. Yet such a route might be less politically possible. Private financing could only take the total expenditure in Britain much higher if the system were changed to include significant private financing through NHI. Otherwise, the NHS is perceived as too good for private care to be worthwhile, except at the margins of general care and for specific needs such as elective surgery. Do we want to spend more? How do we decide? How do we measure the effectiveness of greater expenditure? Are voters serious in wishing to spend more on health care, despite a desire for lower taxes?

If we compare Britain with other Western countries, we can see that we spend a significantly smaller percentage of GDP than most countries on health care (Table A). Looking at publicly financed care only, we still spend proportionately less, except for the US, but to a lesser degree (Table B). This suggests that it may be politically possible to increase public expenditure on health by one or two percentage points of GDP. Beyond that, stimulating more expenditure may require private money.

Table A

Country	% of GDP on Health Care (1987)
Canada	8.6
France	8.6
Netherlands	8.5
Sweden	9.0
UK	6.1
US	11.2

Source: OECD (1990)

Table B

Country	% of GDP Spent Publicly on Health Care (1987)
Canada	6.5
France	6.7
Netherlands	6.6
Sweden	8.2
UK	5.3
US	4.6

Source: Adapted from OECD (1990)

The dilemma is that to get significantly more private money it may be necessary to change from an NHS system to a system where private contributions are part of a nationally regulated insurance system. This in turn will diminish the significant advantages of NHS provision – equity and economy, and, indeed, efficiency.

Sweden is one European country which spends significantly more public money (*c.* 9% of GDP by 1990) on health care. Of course, it has a higher GDP than Britain, and studies have shown that countries spend roughly in proportion to their wealth – poorer countries spend a lower percentage of GDP. Nevertheless, Sweden chooses to spend more than this proportionality would suggest, and does so from the public purse.

Where can Britain go? My own view is that the NHS is the most equitable and efficient system possible. Spending more is worthwhile if results can be demonstrated in terms of better health, or health care, and/or a more satisfied population. Boosting spending by encouraging more private money is less equitable, less effective, and less efficient.

Those who want to transform the NHS by, or replace it with, a competitive system, have to decide whether we are spending too little or too much at present. Are we inefficient? Could we make do with less? Those who decry the NHS's efficiency, by implication arguing it should make do with tighter cost-control, are often the same people who argue for more, less efficient, private care.

OUTCOMES AND OBJECTIVES

How do we therefore define outcomes? If inputs are factors such as numbers of doctors and hospital beds, and outputs are numbers of operations or people served, then outcomes measure the effect on the health status of individuals, groups, or the population as a whole.

A reasonable objective is to seek an amalgam of equity and effectiveness, defined as both improved and equalized health status across the nation. There is no point equalizing a poor outcome, across social classes, for example. Similarly, it is inequitable to seek to maximize outcomes in terms of health status without reference to the distribution of that outcome. Of course, individuals may better be able than others to benefit from an expert-defined outcome.

While a social consensus on goals is needed, the ability of people to benefit may be based on social inheritance. Thus, equity requires imagination in creating hypotheses as to people's potential for benefit and empowerment.

Allocating resources to, and within, health care calls for criteria as to expected result. This is difficult, for factors in society and social policies affect health. Yet, given such complexity, what improvements in health status – for whom – are being sought? How can efficiency be brought to bear, such that the maximum desired result – not necessarily the maximum health status without regard to its distribution – is achieved from available money?

Systems for allocating resources have to measure need, and also take account of the ability of health care to meet that need, even if caring rather than curing or preventing is the order of the day. The need should be met as efficiently as possible, without recourse to exploitation or parsimony in paying and treating workers or poor conditions for patients/consumers.

EFFICIENCY

The different modes of providing care have both advantages and disadvantages, which can be summarized as competitive efficiency *v.* the planned meeting of needs. Whichever one chooses, it is necessary to ensure that the purchasing of care does not give incentives for inefficiency to providers, or lead to results different from those desired. Thus, the balance of power between purchaser and provider is important.

Should there be one global purchaser to ensure provider compliance?

It is in this context that recent debates in Britain can be perceived. Does the formal separation of purchaser and provider mean greater or lesser provider compliance? Does it mean greater or lesser freedom by purchasers to meet populations' needs? Is it sensible in a public health care system to separate financing and provision?

PERSPECTIVE ON PLANNING

This book presents the argument that a publicly planned national health service can be both equitable and efficient. Competitive mechanisms in provision may have a limited place, but the abandonment of public planning would be a retrograde step.

Planning means different things to different people. My uses of the terms are as follows. Indicative planning refers to attempts to harness information on trends, e.g. in the economy, as a basis for possible corrective action. It does not imply public control, development, and siting of services, which I call full-blooded, or substantive, planning. Strategic planning of this sort means scanning the environment to identify factors which will affect one's objectives.

Capital planning – providing or regulating new capital – can be distinguished from revenue planning, where running costs are the focus. In this connection one can distinguish between planning-led resource allocation, where money follows plans, and resource-led plans, where plans are laid after monies have been allocated.

One can distinguish rational, or comprehensive, planning from incremental planning, which argues that only limited understanding, prediction – and change – is possible. Finally, one can distinguish full-blooded planning from a firm's internal business planning, whereby market objectives and opportunities are related to predicted costs and revenues.

The argument presented here is that full-blooded planning is still necessary in the NHS, and can be efficient as well as effective in meeting need. Of course, if planning is perceived as, or allowed to be, by bad management, a mechanistic and unimaginative activity, then it will get a bad name. But planning for social need in health care need not be abandoned just because of assertions by Conservatives that it is a remnant of the evil days of socialism. It is, rather, a necessary part of the armament of the effective general management of the NHS. It should, of course, be flexible. Decisions should not be taken which unnecessarily constrain future choices or options.

Public financing of health care may benefit from a conceptual distinction between planned purchasing by health authorities to meet need and/or demand, and provision. Yet an institutional separation such as that which was proposed in the Prime Minister's Review and the White Paper *Working for Patients*, may be both harmful and counter-productive in a number of ways.

PERSPECTIVE ON POLICY-MAKING

One can distinguish between different modes and styles of policy-making. It may be driven by idealistic or even ideologically minded rational thinkers who are ambitious in setting objectives and devising policy to meet them. (By ideology, I mean a world-view drawing on both alleged facts and values, organized systematically, appealing to a powerful or potentially powerful group in society and having implications for action.)

Alternatively, policy-makers may be mediated by the routines of bureaucracies, such as the Department of Health, or by the competing claims of interest groups, representing, for example, doctors and managers, which have to be reconciled by compromise or log-rolling (vote trading or options trading among different actors and groups whereby less important, favoured options are traded away in order to obtain more important, favoured options).

This book argues that the Prime Minister's Review of the NHS was activated by chance, initially motivated by ideology, then, through various cycles and phases, transformed through mediation by bureaucrats and interests into a rich and unwieldy policy pudding which was, and is, difficult to digest.

Chapter One

Perspectives on different systems: competition and planning

THE CASE OF THE UNITED STATES

It would be misleading to state that the NHS White Paper *Working for Patients* was modelled overtly on US health care. The Prime Minister's Review, while considering a variety of radical options in its early stages, was increasingly forced to accommodate both British political realities and the structure of a public health care system. However, the adoption of the ideas of provider markets and the internal market draws on a misguided perception that US health care is moving towards efficient supply-side competition.

Provider markets refer generally to the possibility of competition in delivering health care, and to the placing by purchasers of contracts for stipulated services. These contracts may be with public or private providers. The purchaser in a British context is generally the district health authority, but in a US context it may be the individual or the employer.

'The internal market' was the phrase adopted by Alain Enthoven (1985) to show that he was proposing a model compatible with public-sector provision, 'internal' referring to the fact that the suppliers are NHS institutions. Enthoven's model draws inspiration from the US in that the district health authority in Britain is seen as capable of adopting some of the characteristics, and reacting to some of the incentives inherent in the US health maintenance organization (HMO), described below.

The key trend in US health care has been the replacement of weak and politically subverted planning in the 1970s by an allegedly pro-competitive strategy in the 1980s. This has sometimes been linked to the phenomenon of for-profit corporate health care (Starr, 1983), although the advances made in the early 1980s by large-scale entrepreneurial health organizations, which were tending to swallow up smaller non-profit organizations, have been halted in the late 1980s due to the high price of allegedly competitive for-profit medicine.

The possible advantages of competition are the provision of health-care services which are more responsive to the consumer, at higher quality and lower prices. In practice these advantages have not necessarily been achieved in the US. The overall cost of health care there remains a major problem. In response to this, a number of new types of financing have been developed, although traditional fee-for-service medicine, reimbursed by the traditional commercial insurer, still plays a significant rôle within the system. Government programmes cover particular categories of the population. The traditional non-profit insurers, such as Blue Cross and Blue Shield still exist, although amended in the direction of greater cost control.

The major development affecting health care is the further expansion of HMOs and their cousins, preferred provider organizations. The aim of these organizations is to contract for more cost-effective health care, and, in some cases, simply cheaper health care. The claim of such programmes to have limited increases in the cost of US health care ought not to be exaggerated, however, as costs continued to rise in the late 1980s, and early 1990s, and indeed have been rising faster than in the mid-1980s. The existence of substantial tax credits for private health care, which cost the federal exchequer more than the whole of the Medicaid programme, hardly encourages cost control, although various mechanisms to limit tax expenditures have been proposed.

In certain areas of the US there is still more regulation than competition, especially in east coast states, such as Massachusetts, New York, New Jersey, and Maryland. However, even where competition has developed, the lessons which can be drawn vary. In some areas of the country the existence of a competitive climate has led to more providers, lower costs, yet a lower quality of health care (by the criterion of avoidable deaths) and less access by the poor, since cross-subsidy to provide charity care for the poor out of rich payers' surpluses is now less possible due to cut-throat competition. This in itself is not an argument against competition, but an argument against competition in the absence of adequate financing for all.

The pluralism in financing of US health care has often meant that only a part of the purchasing market has become competitive, i.e., that part where insurers and payers are cost-conscious, and costs have simply been passed on to less-controlled sections of the market. In some areas of the country, for example, competition does not seem to have affected either the cost of health care, and has perhaps even pushed it up, or the high level of excess capacity in the system. Indeed, by encouraging more providers into the market, excess capacity may be increased. Occupancy rates in US hospitals are generally low in comparison with Europe, the national average being 50–60%. Even when doctors are supposedly in surplus, institutions compete extensively to attract prestigious doctors, and in turn to attract consumers.

Opted-out trust hospitals may do this in Britain by forcing up wages generally for health workers which cannot be replicated in the rest of the NHS. The private purchasing of health care would allow them to do this to a greater extent by injecting new cash. If more money is not forthcoming this US characteristic may not apply in Britain; but high quality of care will not occur either if competition merely entails cost-cutting. Signs in 1991 indicated that trust hospitals were likely to lead to enforced job losses, 're-profiling' (de-skilling) the workforce, and financial cutbacks. These were all the less palatable when combined with huge increases in salaries for trust chief executives and directors of finance.

In the US, competition has apparently led to a reduction in hospitalization. This could, however, be an effect of the general trend in this direction, which has been occurring in any case; or it could be a specific consequence of regulatory policies operating through reimbursement mechanisms, which attempt to contain prices by using methodologies that group illnesses and define expected costs for treating them. So-called 'diagnosis related groups' (DRGs) are the best-known examples of such cost regulations. They are used to price the care of patients in particular disease categories, assembled from groupings of homogeneous diagnoses. They therefore encourage the removal of that patient from hospital as early as possible. Thus, price control may be attributed to powerful factors other than competition between suppliers.

Health maintenance organizations (HMOs)

In the US, the HMOs have been developed to reconcile the incentives confronting the provider and the insurer by merging them into one organization. The HMO receives annual capitations or premiums for its enrolled patients, and in turn is responsible for providing care to them, whether directly or through sub-contracting.

With the HMO, what economists call the problem of the third-party payer is removed by uniting the insurer and the provider. Thus, provider and consumer are no longer equally unconcerned about cost, as long as a third-party payer – the insurer – can foot the bill.

HMOs may be non-profit or for-profit. They may provide services directly through owned facilities and, for example, salaried doctors (in the comprehensive type of HMOs), or they may contract for all the services they provide. However, the dangers of under-supplying care may exist, just as in the traditional private fee-for-service system in the US the danger of over-supply certainly does exist. RAND Corporation studies show that well-funded HMOs do a good, if expensive, job, but that less-well-funded HMOs, such as those used by patients reliant on public funding, can over time adversely affect the health of the elderly, the chronically sick, and the poor (Paton, 1988). Adopting the rationale of the HMO in Britain, as the White Paper seeks to do, is a strategy which requires strict safeguards.

Preferred Provider Organizations are essentially a form of contract, normally between employers on behalf of their employees and stipulated providers, which, due to bulk buying, achieve lower rates of insurance and lower prices for care. The quid pro quo is that the patient is not free to be referred anywhere. Employers furthermore are increasingly providing health insurance directly themselves.

Interestingly enough, federal legislation to promote competition has not been particularly significant. In the late 1960s and early 1970s, legislation to promote planning was half-hearted and eventually stillborn due both to the ideological opposition to planning in the US and to the effect of the American political structure, which has tended to water down health planning and prevent the coherent reconciliation of its different components (Paton, 1990). Competition has been promoted as planning has declined, with its proponents (Enthoven, 1988) arguing that managed health care organizations can promote managed competition that suits the American culture better than planning. It is argued that the pre-planning phase of the 1950s and early 1960s was marked not by competition but by a rigged market, whereby provider 'guilds' colluded with patients at the expense of cost control.

It should be made clear that competition is an American response, and only a partial one, to an American problem. There is no intellectual case for arguing that British planning has similarly failed, and that competitive markets are needed in Britain.

Different types of competition

One should distinguish between competition among providers of health care and competition among financiers (insurers and other payers or reimbursers of health care). In the US it may be that the alleged advantage of competition – high-quality health care for those who have access to the system – stems from the overall level of financing rather than from competition. In copying the American model, there is a danger that Britain would escape the negative side of competition – waste, as a pluralism of payers and financiers is exploited by the providing market – yet would fail to reap the advantage suggested by proponents of competition – high-quality health care responsive to the consumer.

This is because competition in Britain, post-White Paper, is to occur on the supply side. A monopsonistic purchaser (monopolistic power by buyers), with the minor exception of budgets held by GPs, will exist in the form of the district purchaser. In the absence of significantly more resources for health care, the effect upon responsibilities to the consumer is likely to be minimal. It is not the consumer who is sovereign in the post-White Paper NHS, but the district manager as purchaser of health care. That is a major difference from, for example, the newly reformed Dutch health care system, where publicly funded consumers/patients can choose their insurer, prior to the insurer contracting with providers.

MANAGED HEALTH CARE: US AND UK

In recent years, the majority of managerial reforms in US health care have applied to publicly funded programmes, and have embraced attempts to limit cost increases and to restrict access, geared also to cost containment. A central government policy has been the regulation of reimbursement to providers, for example through the system of DRGs. Cost control has also been attempted by directing patients and consumers to stipulated providers. The Medicare and Medicaid programmes have seen a flurry of such regulations in recent years, and costs have been increasingly passed to the patient through deductibles and co-insurance (forms of cost sharing under insurance).

In Britain, the thrust of the White Paper was towards managed health care, with decentralized budget holders (health authority managers and, to a lesser extent, GPs) taking the place of the government at the macro level, and doctors at the micro level in rationing health care on behalf of patients.

Money would now seemingly follow the patient, but the patient would not be free to decide where to go. The patients, in other words, would follow the money, or the contract. Managed health care of this sort would be completely unacceptable politically in the US for the mainstream citizen who currently enjoys access to mainstream US health care. It is only programmes for the poor where this type of restriction prevails. In Britain we have been used to a lower level of funding of health, by no means a disadvantage, as medicalization of life in the US has many costs. But if the trend continues through the type of initiative pursued in the White Paper, private health care as a means of escaping bureaucratic, managed, health care aimed at limiting public expenditure will become more attractive. Thus, while particular individuals may well be sincere in proclaiming that the White Paper is geared to improving the NHS, the long-term social effects must not be discounted.

Rationing

Rationing by people, as opposed to rationing by type of service, although the two can naturally overlap, is more common in the US than in Britain, where rationing is compatible with a supposedly equitable NHS.

In the US, government programmes, mainly through public finance, not public provision, were a partial alternative to the inequities of the market. Yet even in health care the ethos of the market is so strong that when equity and cost control collide due to equity consisting of greater access to an uncontrolled system, equity tends to lose out.

The American system spends much more money in absolute terms, more inefficiently, than the British; it manages to provide much more health care, maybe even absolutely more useful health care. It is difficult to deny that while overall allocation from a central budget which is tightly constrained leads to too much rationing in the NHS, there is a soft underbelly of waste in the US. Both countries, of course, see care being unevenly distributed by geography, speciality, and care group. Yet such unevenness is greater in the US, where a huge total spending goes hand in hand with a dire lack of access for around 40 million people.

A message for Britain

In Britain, before the 1989 White Paper, financial difficulties faced by hospitals or health authorities meant *de facto* rationing, which could vary considerably between regions, districts, and hospitals. This state of affairs has recently attracted wide attention. In a public system such as the NHS, it is of course the case that such rationing is not a do-or-die attempt to stave off financial and actual collapse of the institution. The analogy – exceeding cash limits and so forth – naturally exists, but the consequences of a failure to ration in a financially squeezed district are likely to be the unavailability of budgeted monies for other purposes, whether specialties or whatever, or penalties. That is, rationing one's way out of problems is more readily possible, as a complex web of legal obligations such as those based on American insurance contracts does not exist.

Nevertheless, a conceptual similarity obviously does exist, and the problem of how to reduce inter- and intra-regional discrepancies in susceptibility to rationing is a real and growing one. If equity in the sense of equal access or opportunity for access to care for people at equal risk, or even merely equal opportunity for access to the finance for care (the aim of the resource allocation formula in the NHS), matters at all, the question is a central one.

Prior to the White Paper's implementation, the main advantage of a system whereby individual reimbursements are absent is that rationing does not directly affect those individuals whose insurance is inadequate, or who are complex and expensive cases, and therefore unwelcome under any standard reimbursement system such as DRGs. To link the reimbursement to specific patient care contracts runs the risk of rationing down to the level of individuals and groups. The White Paper embodies changes in this direction.

A GENERAL COMPARISON OF POLICIES AND SYSTEMS

Despite different political traditions, economic situations, and social priorities which affect health policy, insights and warnings from one country to another are naturally important. Countries can learn from each other regarding different methodologies employed to improve public health, and from different forms of organization and agency used to address public health needs.

This section considers the structure of public health policy: the characteristics of health systems and the organization of health services. This includes consideration of the degree of centralism in policy-making and implementation as opposed to devolution; the degree of public financing as opposed to private financing; the degree of public provision as opposed to private provision; and the overall nature of the system. Is it a national health service? Is it a system of national health insurance? Is it a comprehensive or a fragmented system?

Next, we shall consider the degree to which overall health systems planning can be seen as a way of co-ordinating and developing policy for public health. In a number of countries, such as the US and Holland, in the last 20 years there has been a rise and then decline in the apparent attractions of a planning-based approach. Different types of planning are identified, and their goals regarding public health are assessed.

The structure of public health policy

The first important theme in this section is the alleged opposition between centralism and devolution of responsibility for policy in health care systems. One view holds that it is necessary to centralize responsibility for policy within the national government in order to ensure both national objectives and the monitoring of their achievement. Another view holds that the decentralization and devolution of responsibility for policy ensures a more effective link between policy and implementation, and a greater sense of ownership of policy by those directly responsible for service delivery. The two views may not be mutually exclusive, of course, in that centrally defined objectives may be put into practice in varying degrees of decentralization.

A lack of consensus on such a broad matter has been reflected in various health systems over time, or even in cyclical movements between centralization and decentralization. Such movement ought to be interpreted within the context of the structure of the particular health care system. In Britain, for example, a national health service that is publicly financed and broadly publicly provided necessitates the central responsibility for expenditure and allocation of resources, given the derivation of those resources by central government from mostly general taxation.

In the US, a pluralistic and fragmented health-care system, both of financing and provision, linked to a fragmented political system, ensures there is less central allocation of resources, and a correspondingly lesser rôle for central government in determining global criteria for the allocation of resources.

Between these poles one finds what may be termed the national health insurance systems of Western Europe, which combine a significant rôle for public financing and for the private provision of services. The consequence is that the setting of public health objectives by central government may be significant, yet their achievement generally is sought by regulation rather than directly mandated planning of services by government linked to central resource allocation.

The introduction and development of general management in the British NHS illustrates the complexity of the debate concerning centralism and devolution. The lessons which can be learned are of increasing international relevance in an age when the reconciliation of different expensive priorities in many countries with constrained resources implies the need for general management principles.

Following the recommendation of the Griffiths Inquiry in October 1983, some have interpreted general management as a move towards greater central direction of health care objectives and their implementation. Others have seen it primarily as a devolution of responsibility to unit general managers – for example, hospital and community general managers – who are responsible to district and regional general managers, respectively, but who nevertheless have greater day-to-day control than in the pre general-management period.

The original intention behind the creation of the NHS management board was to provide the NHS, which allegedly allows analogies with the large public corporation, with a board of management such as any nationalized industry or public enterprise would have. Responsibility for the NHS would still, however, inevitably lie ultimately with politicians, as before. A sometimes implicit and sometimes explicit separation of management from politics was an important part of the Griffiths agenda.

The management board at the centre would be responsible for the setting of overall objectives for the health service, to be communicated to health authorities and general managers down the line of control, and to be implemented by the latter. Thus, a mix of central control and devolved responsibility for implementation was suggested. The main implication for public-health policy was that consensus management, especially involving the diverse viewpoints of the various health-care professions, was to be replaced by a co-ordinating general management. Existing political lines of control, for example from the Secretary of State to health authority chairman, were not, however, to be replaced.

Neither were existing professional lines of control, for example from the Department of Health's chief medical officer to regional and district medical officers. However, a new line of accountability based on the principles of corporate management was to be added to existing and disparate lines of responsibility.

In practice, the NHS management board was incorporated into the Department of Health and was a less radical initiative than early commentators had expected. Following the February 1989 White Paper *Working for Patients*, the management board was replaced by an NHS management executive responsible to an NHS policy board. This was intended to clear up some of the ambiguity as to whether the Griffiths reforms were about removing politics from the health service, or, indeed, institutionalizing more effective political direction of the health service. Britain will now witness the setting of health-service goals by the politically dominated policy board and the responsibility for their achievement by the NHS management executive, and in particular, its chief executive.

The implications for other countries' public health systems of instituting or reforming general management may be considered. What are the implications for existing clinical priorities? What are the objectives general management is intended to meet? How are these to be monitored? How are efficiency, effectiveness, and equity to be defined? What is the arena for general managers' as opposed to professionals' decision-making (e.g. is it inter-specialty choices as opposed to intra-specialty choices?) What personnel should health authority management teams comprise?

In the US, the complex mosaic of government institutions is responsible for the articulation and implementation of health policy. The system of federalism ensures that the federal government shares power with state governments, and below that, local governments, in making policy. Separation of powers at federal and other levels ensures that policy is often assembled according to the principle of the aggregation of interests rather than top-down central objectives. A publicly financed, publicly provided service as in Britain does not exist.

The main federal responsibility for public health goals lies with the Public Health Service (PHS) within the Department of Health and Human Services. It is the PHS which has been responsible for comprehensive health care and for the goal of preventing disease, as opposed to planning hospital-based or curative health-care delivery systems. The main rôle of the US federal health-care bureaucracy has been to conduct and publicize research, and also to institute significant prevention and promotion programmes, rather than to seek through central resource allocation and provision of services the direct attainment of public health objectives. Traditional curative medicine in the US still dominates the private, fee-for-service system, although there are significant trends, both in the growing for-profit sector and the non-profit sector, to investment in prevention and promotion.

A second important theme concerns the degree to which public financing for health care exists. Where publicly financed health care dominates the health-care system, there is in theory at least the prospect of overt political or managerial choice between broad strategic priorities. That is, the percentage of budget going to curative or acute medicine can be traded off against the amount of money invested in overt public health programmes such as preventive and promotive programmes based on epidemiological research, and programmes of care for chronic conditions. There is, however, no guarantee this will be done in practice or through a 'rational' methodology. For central determination of objectives masks the question of who determines objectives, and why and how objectives are determined. Domination of the policy-making machinery by traditional providers can be envisaged, or by partial political viewpoints of whatever variant.

In decentralized political and health-care systems, where public financing is either less evident or less centralized, it is likewise an open question as to who dominates the decision-making machinery, although the means of so doing will be different.

Political science and sociology offer us paradigms such as pluralism, élitism, and Marxism, which can be applied to the health arena in an attempt to explain public policy. Pluralism argues that power is spread, if not equally then adequately. The US system is decentralized; Britain's is centralized. Both could be pluralistic in that whatever the level of decision-making, it could be open to a variety of social influences from different parties, groups, and classes. That is, one should not confuse pluralism or its absence with centralism or decentralization – they are different discussions.

However, the US and Britain may not be pluralistic, if one believes that élites dominate policy-making, whether centrally or in decentralized decision-making fora. The US has many biases in the political system to fragmented policy, which hinders progressive reform and benefits élites (Paton, 1990). Britain allows more effective, centrally planned reform through its more cohesive system, but allows élite domination of its top-heavy executive through informal establishment channels.

Marxism and other so-called radical perspectives argue that policy may be biased to the interests of an economically based ruling class, however internally heterogeneous that class is. In today's world, it may make more sense to talk not of one ruling class, but of different sectors sharing interests and ideologies. For example, the forces making up what was the Thatcherite coalition comprised traditional capitalists, small businessmen, affluent workers and others who believe that they may be 'better off' in a 'low tax' market economy.

In health care, it is important to examine who controls both policy-making and the implementation of policy, e.g. in Britain, the machinery of the Department of Health and the NHS. That is, how does power affect social outcomes?

Just because a system is decentralized does not automatically mean it is less public or more dominated by private interests (Nordlinger, 1981), but in practice there is a high correlation between such characteristics.

The third important theme is the degree of public provision of health care. At one end of the spectrum is health care, characterized by largely publicly owned hospitals and community services. At the other end of the spectrum is the system characterized by for-profit private providers. In between, one finds systems dominated by voluntary or non-profit but private providers, as in much of Europe; varying degrees of regulation and control of private providers; and varying obligations of private providers to combine publicly stipulated objectives with their own self-determined institutional objectives.

Taken together, these three themes have a strong bearing on a fourth theme, which concerns the overall nature of the health care system. Again, thinking in terms of a spectrum, we have the public NHS at one end, and the conceptual opposite of the wholly privately financed, wholly privately providing system at the other end – an extreme which is an ideal type rather than a characterization of any country's existing health system.

The various permutations in between are best thought of in terms of how they combine public or private financing and provision of services; how they combine central versus local determination of objectives; how they combine central or local mobilization and allocation of resources; and the degree to which they are characterized by interventionist criteria for the planning or regulation of services. Apart from what might be termed the political economy and structural aspects of the health-care system, one can also analyse the system in terms of its global allocation of resources between acute and curative medicine; caring and chronic services, including community care; and preventive or promotive health services. Naturally, in a public system these choices are overt and global, whereas in a system characterized by large-scale private financing and consumption of health care such choices will be determined by the priorities of individuals, groups, businesses, and trade unions, rather than politicians and managers. In the US, for example, health care coalitions of business, unions and/or consumers, are increasingly trying to influence costs and priorities in the health-care market.

Planning as a means of co-ordinating strategies for public health

Planning naturally covers a multitude of activities. The 'strong' definition of planning adopted here is the determination of the pattern and mix of services, both spatial/geographical and qualitative, to serve acknowledged principles of distribution and redistribution of services, and the corresponding determination of strategy to achieve that pattern of services. Such planning may well involve public provision, and will be stronger than mere regulation.

There are different philosophies of planning. Rational, or full-blooded, planning has frequently been contrasted with incrementalist planning, with the mixed scanning approach seen as a compromise of sorts between these two extremes. Different approaches to planning involve different actors: some planning processes, whether deliberately or not, are politically dominated; others are intended to be dominated by the neutral scientists. Some systems of planning are in effect subservient to systems of resource allocation, in that resources may be allocated by a formula or methodology which is geared specifically to identifying the need for services.

One can therefore have planning which is subservient to resource allocation. Alternatively, one can have resource allocation which is subservient to planning: decisions can be taken about a pattern of services, including hospitals, community services, primary care, and preventive services. Capital budgets and revenue budgets are determined accordingly, and in consequence the resource allocation across the region in question is effectively determined, or at least constrained.

Thinking along lines such as these tends to assume a central body – whether a country's department of health or health region – which has a responsibility for global planning or resource allocation. In a system dominated by private health insurance, private purchase of health care and, for example, private subscription to prepaid organizations such as the HMOs in the US, global planning in this sense will not exist. Planning in this context will tend to refer instead to indicative or technical planning within the providing organization to gear its services to market demand.

Broadly speaking, comprehensive health service planning has developed in various countries with a view to measuring the need for different types of services, and to redistributing resources across countries and across regions where necessary to achieve this. In practice, however, it is not surprising that lofty goals will often not be met. In the US, there was a move from the mid-1960s to the late 1970s to incorporate a form of planning into the largely private system. Hospital development programmes after the Second World War, such as the Hill-Burton Act of 1946, were followed by the Regional Medical Programmes Act 1965, the Comprehensive Health Planning Act of 1966, and, more significantly, the National Health Planning and Resources Development Act of 1974. In practice, however, planning has not been global: it has been capital-based; it has been voluntaristic rather than mandatory, increasingly into the 1980s; and it has been diverted from public health goals by provider coalitions at the level of the planning agency (the health systems agency).

Both original proponents and opponents of planning were disappointed in results; and planning has generally been discredited, with a move to a renewed faith in competition within the US health system as a way of increasing efficiency by providers, and therefore making the extension of access more affordable on the financing side. This has raised a lively debate about whether profit-seeking health-care institutions are cheaper and more cost-effective, or the reverse.

In the US, the decline of planning is not a criticism of planning *per se*, but of the conservative US polity's inability to handle well progressive reform in social policy, which requires social planning and economic redistribution. It is an irony that Britain is moving to copy the US when its current stance reflects its own failures, and is not in any way solving the key problems of the health system, the foremost of which is unfairness and often cruelty – not too strong a word.

Planning in many countries has not been concerned simply with cost control, but with the extension of access to a more affordable health care system once planning had curbed the expense of the traditional fee-for-service medical market, as in the US. Both in the US and in the Netherlands, however, planning has developed into a restrictive activity, with resources development and redistribution very much down-played in recent years.

There are thus a number of dimensions on which planning can be categorized. It can be comprehensive or incremental; it can address capital budgets, revenue budgets, or both – even through a merging of the two. Indeed, a major problem in health planning systems has often been that planned revenue budgets have not been consistent with implications of planned capital budgets. Thus, we have had the phenomena of new hospitals without budgets to run them; or, at the other extreme, revenue budgets with no meaningful services on which they can be spent.

As always, it is dangerous to compare idealized or ideologically based pictures with their real-world opposites: idealized competition compared with real-world planning, warts and all; or real-world competition, warts and all, compared with idealized planning. Accepting insights from both philosophies may be useful. For example, using the planning process to simulate markets whereby primary care physicians refer patients for secondary care according to consumer choice as well as their own priorities, to allow modelling and construction of a planning system to site, extend, or contract facilities in line with such referral patterns, may be a promising means of proceeding. Thus, health authorities can combine a strategic rôle, yet avoid a heavy-handed or bureaucratic top-down approach.

All in all, the benefit of preserving a planned NHS is a clear lesson from foreign, especially US, experience. The advantages of the US are not yet realized there, let alone transferable to Britain. In aggregate, the US does not have a competitive system as much as a system dominated by powerful interests that obstruct naïvely interpreted, textbook markets.

COMPETITION AND CONSUMERISM:
OPTIONS IN FINANCING AND PROVIDING HEALTH CARE

Choice by whom?

Prior to the White Paper *Working for Patients*, patients in Britain had the right to be referred anywhere within the NHS system by their GP. Given greater demand – many would argue, greater need – for services than could be supplied under existing finances, such freedom of referral did not of course guarantee care. People might be referred only to be placed by hospital consultants on waiting-lists. Furthermore, GPs might be less likely to refer those who they thought the system was incapable of treating, whether for financial or other reasons.

The title of the White Paper, *Working for Patients*, implied a greater stress upon the rights of the patient, now to be known as the consumer of health care. The problem was that the essence of the White Paper separated the financing of health care from the provision of health care. Health authorities, and GP practices which elected to hold their own budgets for selective categories of hospital care, were to purchase care, but not necessarily provide it themselves. Where they did provide it themselves, through their own directly managed units, an artificial distinction was to be made between the purchasing and the providing halves of the health authority. The fact that the individual was not the purchaser meant that any new consumerism in the NHS was not to be based on the individual's purchasing rights.

Giving purchasing rights directly to the individual while preserving public financing of health care would require individuals to be given health vouchers, which would allow the individual to buy care from whichever source he or she wished. In practice, there would be limitations, but in theory the voucher could include access to primary care (GPs) on the one hand, and hospital and community services on the other.

The main problem is that giving people vouchers would have to be done on actuarial principles, yet in ignorance of the actual need that these people would face. Old people would require vouchers worth more; potentially sick people would require vouchers worth more; and so forth. The advantage of allocating to health authorities comprising large populations, whether as purchasers or as purchasers and providers jointly, would be lost in that risks could not be spread and averaged out over time. Some people would find their vouchers unused at the end of the year or partially unused; others would run out of voucher credit.

It is interesting to note that such were the problems anticipated when the former Secretary of State for Social Services, John Moore, attempted to promote the idea, during the Prime Minister's Review of the NHS in 1988, of allowing people to contract-out of the NHS; that is, in effect giving them a voucher, given that they had contracted in compulsorily to the NHS through taxation and national insurance, to be used to buy private insurance. This idea was carbon-copied from the government's policy at the time to encourage private pensions.

Assuming the same amount of money is in the system and is used for roughly the same purposes at the same level of efficiency, separating the purchaser from the provider of health care was merely a means of transferring the responsibility for rationing care, or making hard choices about priorities when seeing individual patients, from hospital consultants to the health authorities responsible for purchasing the care. But it would not be the patients who were making such choices.

In the US, HMOs (comprehensive systems which own their own facilities and employ their own doctors and other health care staff) generally have rules about where patients can and cannot be referred. The first point of contact in those HMOs which employ what the Americans call a 'primary physician gatekeeper' is the GP, who has a contract with the HMO and therefore abides by these rules of referral and non-referral. Thus, while freedom of referral is limited, there is not a separation between the purchaser and the provider of health care. The essence of the HMO is that it is the financier, or special kind of insurance company, and also the provider. The separation of course lies between the consumer and the financier; the consumer in the US is, at least in theory, free to choose between competing HMOs or other forms of health care. In practice, of course, there are not enough HMOs to make that a meaningful choice in most parts of the country as yet.

In the Netherlands, following the government's partial acceptance of the Dekker Report (Dekker, 1987), consumers will increasingly choose between insurance companies and sick-funds, which will then contract with providers. The health reforms of the Netherlands are geared to fulfilling a number of objectives.

Firstly, public insurance is still in effect a payroll, health-specific tax, as the government pays the premium to insurance companies and sick-funds, which people choose to join – out of national insurance contributions by workers, firms, and the state. That is, the individual does not choose which fund (purchaser) to join on the basis of price, except now at the margin, for the Dekker reforms have allowed limited price competition between funds/insurers based on top-up money paid by the individual.

Secondly, the distinction between sick-funds (non-profit) and insurance companies (for-profit) will gradually disappear, as all are now competing for a universal clientele. In the old system, the richest 40% of the population insured themselves privately, while the state system covered enrolment in the sick-funds.

Thirdly, the new insurers – increasingly, merged companies whereby sick-funds unite with insurers – will compete for customers, whereas in the old system one generally enrolled with the local fund or company. The aim is therefore to promote consumer choice as to purchaser: the purchaser offering the citizens best judgement of need and priorities will attract the customer.

As with the old system, the problem is that if consumers can join whatever insurer they wish and be referred wherever they like (currently, a treasured part of the system), in effect, cost-control is impossible. The government will have to pay retrospectively as in the old system for whatever care the sick-funds pay for. In the old system, the funds were really just open-ended, government third-party payers.

If competition is to instil efficiency, insurers/purchasers will have to have contracts with preferred providers, or even own them, as in HMOs. Consumers will then choose their purchasers according to the latter's ability to negotiate with providers to provide a good, comprehensive deal. This will be either a good package of care for the standard rate, if there is no price competition, or cost-effective care, which is therefore cheaper for a standard amount of care or only a little more expensive for extra services if there is price competition, albeit limited.

Thus if the government does not simply finance whatever is provided and consumed by behaving as a third-party payer without incentives to restraint, then a market can work. It will be based on choice of purchaser with either competition as to services and quality or price competition, or as intended, a bit of both, with price competition being allowed at the margin.

Whichever mix applies, it is clear that a closer link between purchaser and provider is envisaged to prevent contracting labyrinths and attempts by the provider to manipulate the purchaser. That is, a purchaser/ provider split may often mean the inability of the purchaser to determine need and achieve its meeting due to market unpredictability, and in particular, provider capture. This was paradoxically the reason allegedly behind the creation of the purchaser/provider split in Britain – to end the old system's provider capture. However, the scope for it may be greater, post-White Paper.

It is more than ironical, therefore, that the White Paper proposed a separation between the financier/purchaser of health care and the provider. There may be advantages to this at the margin or in special circumstances, however, in general this merely means the creation of an artificial market which has to be policed at great expense. The bureaucratic costs of running the market after 1991 led to much disillusionment, even among doctors who had formed the minority of the medical profession in favour of the reforms.

Where in Britain, under the White Paper arrangements, does the consumer win? The consumer has lost rights to be referred generally throughout the system, as it is alleged to be either too expensive or, in the context of a cash-limited NHS, too destructive of priorities, which it is alleged ought to be made by purchasing authorities rather than settled after the event by doctors desperately trying to ration care through waiting-lists, which may stem from a lack of capacity to provide treatment through absence of equipment, as well as through queues for scarce appointments and hospital stays.

There may be more choice for the purchasing authority if a market, however phoney or artificial, is created whereby purchasers can choose among providers. The reason a market may well be phoney, as long as providers are in effect controlled by health authorities or in some senses by the Department of Health – or are accountable through the parliamentary process to bodies such as the House of Commons' Public Accounts Committee – is that the purchasers are bound to protect local services to some extent. Thus, paradoxically, a market may in fact merely mean a contracting for local services. Providers may either be monopolies or may indulge in monopolistic competition whereby they are selling themselves as a result of fulfilling a particular niche in the market – supplying what the particular purchaser wants and cannot find from another provider. Nevertheless, in such a system there may be some sort of freedom accorded to purchasers to choose.

It seems that if purchasers in Britain are to have a choice among providers, or are to have the rôle of rationing care through deciding what their own local providers may provide, if the purchasing/providing split is not considered important, there is still a need to decide how consumers are to have a choice. On paper, in conjunction with the GP, the old system allowed them to choose which hospital and community health services they wanted to use. However, this was more a theoretical than a practical right for most people. A possibility, rather than thinking of choice in terms of place of referral, would be to think of choice in terms of first point of contact with the health care system; consumers could then choose their GP with greater ease. That is part of the thrust of the White Paper, although exactly how it will work in practice is still not clear.

This in itself may not be very important if GPs' referrals are constrained by where the purchasing authority has placed contracts for care. The purchasing health authority will only tolerate referrals by the GP, which do not form part of the purchasing authority's contract with providers, where they are unavoidable – in cases of emergency, for example, just as in the case of American HMOs, which will sanction extra-contractual referrals in cases of emergency. Otherwise, the contracting system constrains freedom.

The only alternative is for the contracting system to be a charade whereby GPs are free to refer where they like, and contracts are somehow placed to accommodate this. Those referrals which cannot be predicted are simply paid out of the health authority's reserves. The main problem here is that the growth of reserves will mean that actual contracts out of non-reserve money, or the main part of the budget, will be contracts for a total quantum of care less than the total budget available for health care.

Allowing the patient to choose the GP, if the GP is not part of the organization which places contracts for care (i.e. not in a budget-holding practice), is not particularly meaningful. The option therefore is to give budgets for all or most health care to GPs, who then buy in services from stipulated hospitals and community units, whether these are competing in any meaningful sense or not. There are of course practical and logistical problems with regard to this, and also problems concerning the current culture of GPs, many of whom could not cope with such responsibility. An alternative, however, is to allow consumers to choose which purchasing authorities they belong to, and to ensure that GPs themselves have to contract with such purchasing authorities, acting as gatekeepers in the further referral of patients, except in cases of emergency and other such circumstances, to the providers stipulated by the purchaser, whether or not this is done through a genuinely competitive market. The argument here is that since free referral without the system is not possible if cash limits and a limited budget for the NHS are to be reconciled with priorities made by purchasing authorities, at least the consumer can choose which purchasing authority to belong to. The choice would presumably be made in terms of which purchasing authorities established the best reputation for providing quality care.

In the US the private consumer will decide which HMO to join on the basis of cost as well as quality. In the context of a publicly financed NHS, however, cost would not be the criterion for deciding which health authority to join. Instead, those which, with their available resources – based on the resources they receive according to the populations they have enrolled and the age and morbidity characteristics of these populations – are seen to have the best record will be the ones that attract the most patients. This would of course break the current condition whereby the health authority to which one belongs is defined simply by its geographical boundaries. Currently, one's health authority depends on where one lives; one can imagine the crazy situation in which somebody who lives in London elects to join Inverness Health Authority. Nevertheless, such a policy might apply at the margin, just as it is argued that the beneficial effect of market forces generally in the NHS will be at the margin, rather than diffused throughout the system as the essence of the system. The British reforms would then be closer to the recent Dutch reforms. Consumerism would not just be a bureaucrat's buzz-word.

In the end, all of this might mean a lot of bureaucratic tinkering in pursuit of fairly abstruse theory. It could well be argued that the best way of guaranteeing more meaningful patient choice is by choice of GP, plus guaranteed free referral, and adequate resources to ensure that such referrals could be handled. Whereas the former solution seems artificial, the latter solution seems a little Utopian in a climate of harsh realism concerning financial spending limits. In practice it would not be significantly different from a system of national health insurance whereby hospitals were publicly owned (or at least non-profit, if private and autonomous) and the citizen could expect coverage for most if not all conditions. Such rationing as there was, might be done with greater public consensus (public debates are only just beginning in Britain as awareness of rationing spreads from the closed world of politicians).

To summarize, the different approaches to providing consumer choice and financing health care are:

- To allow the patient to choose the provider, whether or not in consultation with a GP, and ensure finance to pay for it through a British-style NHS; or through private payment and insurance.
- To ensure that the purchasing authority has the right to choose the provider for the patient whether through a post-White-Paper contracting process as in Britain; or a US-style HMO; and whether or not the purchaser/provider link is loosened, as in post-White-Paper Britain; or tightened or unified, as in certain HMO models.
- To allow the consumer to choose the purchaser and then operate as in the above whether in US-style HMO; or by allowing the consumer to choose which health authority to belong to, with geographical constraints limiting the patients to their local health authority, being loosened.

The key difference between the American HMO and the post-White-Paper British purchasing district is that the HMO unites the purchaser/financier/insurer and the provider, whereas the district seeks to separate those roles. It is an irony that the British reforms were inspired in part by the HMO idea, yet loosened this HMO characteristic which had already existed in the NHS, pre-White Paper.

The next chapter takes us back in time to review the structure of the British NHS, and seeks to explain the reasons for the White

Paper and new agenda for policy-makers and managers in the 1990s. Having done this, the logic of the White Paper and unfolding events early in the 1990s can then be set against the options thus far reviewed.

Chapter Two

The legacy: the NHS and its problems in perspective

The British National Health Service, in existence since 1948, has evolved from its early days through a number of formal and informal reorganizations which have been in pursuit of both policy and managerial changes.

At the outset, the NHS's hospital service was organized separately from primary services, and many community services fell within the responsibility of local government rather than the health service.

It was only in 1974 that the first major reorganization attempted to integrate hospital and community health services. General practice, the most important constituent of primary care, remained separate, with GPs paid by capitation as independent contractors by Family Practitioner Committees (FPCs), which administered the Family Practitioner Services (FPSs).

One unforeseen consequence of the reorganization was to split up community services, e.g. care of client groups such as the elderly and mentally handicapped, between local authorities and the community health services. Thus, the aims of the 1974 reorganization – integration of services, and reforms to management structures allegedly to combine both rational management and consensual decision-making – were only partially met. The new unity of hospital and community services was often only a unity on paper and in the organization chart on the civil servant's desk.

In 1982 another reorganization occurred, again under a Conservative Government, although the previous one had incorporated ideas from the pre-1970 Labour Government. This time the aims were more directly managerial. In 1974 the new unified HCHS had incorporated regional, area, and district tiers of government. The 1982 reform removed areas, acting in the belief that the 1974 structure was too bureaucratic and cumbersome.

As expressed in the government document *Patients First*, another major aim was decentralization of responsibility, not only for implementation but also for local policy, which fitted in with the ideology of the new government in its first phase. The stress of the mid-1970s Labour Government on community services, the priorities of chronic client group care, and community care as an alternative to institutionalization, was preserved.

Only one and a bit years later, however, the NHS was in the throes of another reorganization in all but name, the consequences of the Griffiths Management Inquiry, which advocated general management as a corporate model for both individual health authorities and the central apex of the NHS, hitherto only administered by DHSS civil servants imbued with a lay and generalist ethos (Griffiths, 1983). The aim was to provide a management board for the NHS analogous to those presiding over and directing large-scale corporations, both public and private.

This further change represented a swing back to centralized control, as the Conservatives discovered that the ideology of decentralization could not guarantee control over their social objectives. Whereas the Griffiths reforms cannot be classed simply as centralism as they give genuine scope for greater local responsibility for implementation, they represent an increased interest in central monitoring of targets, especially in relation to resource management, value for money, and efficiency in the NHS.

The hospital and community health services are cash limited, depending upon the size of the overall budget given to the NHS through the direct taxation and national insurance contributions, which the Exchequer then allocates to health after Cabinet decision and the Public Expenditure Survey process. The NHS is funded through public finance, and provided mainly through public provision. However, the FPSs were not cash limited before 1990: while the small sum for administration of FPSs was cash limited, the actual budgets for drugs and certain services were influenced by demand by doctors.

The major consequence of the separation of the HCHS and FPS is that there is an incentive for the cash-limited services (HCHS) to offload patients to the FPS. Worries about open-ended FPS budgets led in 1985–6 to the implementation of a limited list of drugs from which NHS GPs have to select their treatment, which was a controversial move. Thus, the NHS is free at the point of use in the HCHS, being a public service; fast-rising prescription charges and charges for optical and dental care, however, have removed this epithet from the FPS.

The process for distributing resources to the NHS, even after the White Paper, is based on a canon of equity: namely, that there should be equal opportunity for access to the finance for health care for those at equal risk. There is no overt measure of outcome in the formula, however – hardly surprising as no health system distributes systematically according to either effectiveness or efficiency, even were such a utilitarian system to be ethically acceptable, with its often troublesome implications for equity. The British system is more advanced than any other system in the world, but this does not mean it is perfect.

If outcome is to be addressed, this means considering overall health status, and also the contributions of specific medical/health policy interventions to the ends of individual and population health.

Inequalities of health in Britain between classes and regions, while no worse than in many other countries, have remained worrying (Black, 1980; Whitehead, 1987; Townsend *et al.*, 1988). They have not been caused by the NHS, however; were it not for the NHS, they would have been worse. Social, environmental, economic, and politically determined causes of ill health can only be partially addressed by a health system. And of course the British NHS, by comparison with other Western European countries, spends relatively little on total health care. (The NHS provides *c*. 94% of total health care, as measured by resources; the private sector is only really significant for elective surgery, where it provides *c*. 25%.)

To reduce inequalities and to increase the efficiency and productiveness of the health system, it is likely that better co-ordination of curative and, more particularly, preventive and promotive care will be necessary, along with general reduction of social inequality, material deprivation, and social deprivation.

CURE, CARE, OR PREVENTION?

The NHS has often been criticized as a sickness service rather than a health service, the implication being that there is too much stress on cure rather than prevention and promotion, and even care. This debate, however, has by and large remained at the level of values and general exhortation. Detailed comparisons of outcome, effectiveness, quality, efficacy, efficiency, and equity in the different types of service have not been made.

A series of official policy statements and government circulars in the 1970s articulated a change in priorities towards chronic care and the care of specific client groups such as the elderly, the mentally handicapped, and the mentally ill. In particular, *Priorities for Health and Personal Social Services* (DHSS, 1976a) and *The Way Forward* (DHSS, 1977) made this case. The Conservative Party won the 1979 general election, and the policy of care in the community for priority groups was reaffirmed (*Care in the Community*, (DHSS, 1981)). This circular was accompanied by *Care in Action* (DHSS, 1981), which was a handbook of policies and priorities for the health and personal social services in England.

Naturally, a growing interest in non-acute and non-hospital care has been increasingly controversial. At times of faster expansion, or at least growth, in the NHS budget, a change in priorities is easier as no sector necessarily loses in real terms. In recent years, however, it has become increasingly clear that significant practical commitment to the priority services will mean real problems for the acute and high-technology sectors of medicine. Just as the Resource Allocation Working Party (RAWP) procedures for resource allocation, would have been less controversial if their first ten years of operation (1976–86) had seen more money allocated to the NHS overall, the same has characterized the acute-versus-chronic debate. Redistribution, whether in terms of overall resources by formulae or in terms of discrete policy choices, is tougher when the losers lose more significantly, or absolutely, rather than just relatively. A lack of economic growth necessitates 'robbing Peter to pay Paul'.

Even advocates of balanced strategies to tackle the health effects of social problems have criticized the often-implicit assumption that the acute services must bow to vaguely constituted programmes for prevention. Growth in acute services may not have been because of bad planning but as a direct response to perceived need.

Hence, the policy debate has sharpened. The perceived crisis – whether it be that or not – in NHS funding in 1987–8 led some on both the political left and right to advocate that the NHS should concentrate more on acute problems such as those highlighted by waiting-lists, and inversely leave the less clinical function to local government authorities, voluntary agencies, and private and domestic care.

Others have advocated that greater spending on primary, preventive, and community care is desirable; and that many of the acute sector's demands are based on treatments with low efficacy, poor outcomes and/or a poor cost/effectiveness record.

COMMUNITY AND PRIMARY CARE

On this issue, a number of policies were under consideration in the late 1980s. The Audit Commission – a body delegated by Parliament to monitor value for money in the public sector, a task which has increasingly involved it in policy analysis rather than mere accounting – reported on the poor co-ordination and fragmentation of sources of financing for community care (Audit Commission, 1986). This produces perverse incentives and inappropriate care, often in the wrong settings, for clients such as the elderly and mentally handicapped.

In response, the government asked Sir Roy Griffiths of the NHS Management Inquiry to produce a policy statement. This sought to clarify responsibilities for certain types of care, with an enlarged rôle for local authorities, not necessarily accompanied by resources, in caring for groups with less direct call on clinical, as opposed to nursing and other caring services. The result was the White Paper *Caring for People* (Department of Health, 1989c). The National Health Service and Community Care Bill of 1989 sought to implement the Paper, which accepted some but not all of Griffiths' conclusions, as well as the major White Paper,

Working for Patients (DoH, 1989a). However, by the end of 1990 it was clear that delays in implementing new proposals for community care would occur for political reasons.

In primary care, a White Paper from the DHSS in November 1987 had expanded on earlier consultation documents, as well as incorporating some suggestions from the Royal College of General Practitioners, in advocating more task-related payments for GPs and a variety of incentives to efficiency, including the promise, or threat, of greater competition by GPs for patients.

GPs have been paid by capitation, with extra reimbursement for the elderly and for certain services (e.g. cervical cytology, paid by fee-for-service). The new proposals herald a great weighting for task-based procedures, including prevention and population screening, and a lesser weighting for general capitation-based reimbursement. The White Paper of 1989 was accompanied by a proposed new contract for FPs which, however, increased the significance of capitation, the number of patients thereby having a greater rôle in determining a GP's pay. It is not surprising that GPs felt that government initiatives were mushrooming faster than logic suggested.

GPs are independent contractors, and the separation of the primary care service from the hospital and community services is bemoaned by some as diminishing the scope for effective planning of global services in the light of both need and demand.

Another problem is that central government may often adopt and seek to implement specific initiatives in primary care in the field of prevention and promotion, e.g. new national guidelines for cervical cytology screening, yet often fail to ensure that these mandatory initiatives are accompanied by any extra money from the government. As a result, health authorities will inevitably have to poach money from other programmes. This can occasionally have advantages, but it is at least arguable that the disadvantages outweigh the advantages of such arbitrary central intervention without resources.

THE POLITICS OF HEALTH POLICY

Before the late 1980s, the NHS enjoyed considerable political consensus in Britain. It was created by a Labour government; ideas incorporated in the original NHS were drawn from members of other political parties and members of no party; and significant changes in later years have been managerial rather than directly political in import.

The essence of the NHS is its use of centrally collected public resources to provide health care through public provision. Over the years, significant attempts have been made to direct resources to areas, groups, and individuals of greatest need. To this end, the NHS naturally embodies elements of socialist principle.

The NHS has been acceptable to many Conservatives in that it accords with the more paternalistic view of welfare, as compared with, for example, conservatives in the US whose primary allegiance tends to be to market liberalism. The most persistent criticism of the NHS has indeed come from market liberals, who argue that the NHS does not operate through market principles – by which they mean a free market characterized by many providers of service and many purchasers – and therefore cannot provide the alleged advantages of a market.

With the exception of full-blooded market liberals, however, both the theory and practice of the NHS can be incorporated into different ideologies, and it has therefore been acceptable through a variety of political perspectives. More pragmatically, the NHS has become a highly popular British institution. Only at their peril would political parties seek to oppose it; which is what makes the events leading up to the White Paper of 1989 so interesting, as well as so difficult to unravel.

Major criticisms of the NHS have tended to be made from a position of support for the service, whether thorough-going or half-hearted. Naturally, those on the left tend to argue most for significantly greater resources for the service. Those on the right tend to stress fiscal restraint and the need to limit expectations about what the NHS can deliver. The more extreme versions of this perspective see the NHS as a kind of welfare safety net in health care, albeit available universally.

Both Labour and Conservative governments from 1948 to the present day have found difficulty in reconciling demand for health care with available resources. The demands of the economy as a whole have often dictated NHS policy. The Treasury in particular has played a dominant rôle in debate with the Department of Health concerning priorities and flexibility, or lack of it, in using capital and revenue resources.

Some on both the left and right have perceived a fiscal crisis in welfare policy as a whole, affecting the NHS, based on the tension between tax revenues and demands upon government expenditure. Those on the left tend to argue that a capitalist economy has difficulty in reconciling incentives to private business through low taxation, spending on the infrastructure of the economy and spending on welfare. Those on the right argue that economic strategy as a whole depends on a low-tax economy, with expectations as to government spending tailored accordingly, and greater individual responsibility wherever possible for welfare, including health care.

By international standards, most perspectives in debates concerning health care in Britain stress centralization, and this reflects the structure of the British political system. The NHS is financed largely from general taxation, and Ministers are directly responsible to Parliament for the service. As well as causing difficulties for attempts to establish autonomous management structures for the NHS, this central feature has ensured that no political party has aimed either to place responsibility for health care upon the individual or the employer, as in the US, or unequivocally to advocate a back seat for politicians in the minutiae of health care decision-making.

Within the NHS some have perceived power to be held by élites rather than by a community, as represented indirectly by health authorities and managers before the White Paper – and not at all after it. The medical profession has been seen by some commentators as a dominant interest; while more radical commentators have argued that overall policy is determined by the dictates of the capitalist economy. Apart from general theory of these sorts, recent debates have concerned the relative power of health managers, health authorities, the community, and the various professions which together deliver what is a complex service provided by a complex organization. Overall, most health systems have as their central challenge the provision of health care to acceptable standards of equity at acceptable levels of cost and expenditure. The US has traditionally had the least to say about overall social equity, addressing the problems of those, especially the poor, who lack access, in a very piecemeal manner. Most systems, however, seek to reconcile access and cost at the macro level. This leads automatically to debates about the best means of, firstly, financing health care, and, secondly, of providing it. It is indeed the distinction between financing and provision which lies at the heart of the recent reforms in Britain.

Debates about financing and provision lead on to more detailed debates about systems of resource allocation and planning. In centralized public systems such as Britain, this leads to debates about methodology for allocating resources and for planning services. In less centralized systems, such as many of those in Europe which operate through health insurance, resources may depend upon individual employer and state contributions, and therefore central allocative mechanisms have been less central. Nevertheless, these systems also may incorporate aspects of central planning and resource allocation.

The main influences upon health policy in aggregate may be said to derive from ideologies and social culture; political structures in the country in question; the behaviour of political parties; and the behaviour of interest groups, pressure groups, academic and advisory groups, and a variety of informal as well as formal inputs to the policy making process.

THE EVOLVING NHS: PRESSING PROBLEMS

Between 1948 and the early 1960s, many of NHS management's current concerns were not significant issues. There were no formalized planning procedures; there was no systematic system for resource allocation from the Department of Health to regions (and from the Scottish, Welsh and Northern Ireland offices to their respective areas); and there was no systematic theory or practice of management underpinning the Service. This is hardly surprising, as the early priorities of the Service were to take into public ownership formerly voluntary or local authority hospitals, and to meet the new demands for health care which were registering within the system. The Guillebaud Committee of 1956 had basically given the evolving NHS a vote of approval in response to worries that it was costing too much, an ironical situation when one considers today's levels of expenditure.

In 1962, the so-called 'hospital plan' embraced the philosophy of core general hospitals, later to be known as district general hospitals, for districts over the country, and represented an early and crude attempt at planning for the capital requirements of the national health service on a geographical basis. That is to say, it identified where new hospitals and facilities might be needed. Towards the end of the 1960s, moves were taken by the Secretary of State for Social Services, Richard Crossman, to establish a methodology for allocating resources to the health regions of England, based at this time on the old regional hospital boards, on the basis of need for health care. An approach was adopted which combined measures of population and use of services.

The 1974 reorganization, following a blueprint designed by McKinsey Management Consultants, advocated new management structures for the NHS which accepted the concept of the administrative team of officers working through consensus management, yet attempted to systematize relationships between the centre and the new regions, areas and districts, which were set up to manage health care provision, including the new community health services. By common consent this produced an over-bureaucratic and top-heavy structure for the Service. In 1982 the Conservative government, in its earlier days following a model of decentralization, abolished the areas, and, following the patients first document, located management responsibility at the level of the district, as well as encouraging non-statutory forms of care.

Between these two reorganizations, the Resource Allocation Working Party (RAWP) had reported in 1976. The halfway house instituted by Richard Crossman for allocating resources was crude, and it had been the remit of the RAWP, chaired by John C.C. Smith, Under-secretary at the Department of Health and Social Security, to design a new approach to allocating resources based on the equitable principle of giving equal opportunity for access to health care for those at equal risk of disease.

The Griffiths prescription for general management at the centre of the Service, as well as in health authorities, seemed at the time to threaten the traditional Civil Service lay administration. While the permanent secretary was personally in favour of a better-managed service (Stowe, 1988), he was at the time successful in limiting the radical implications of the Griffiths reforms at the apex of the NHS. It was, however, the political imperative which thwarted the forlorn idea of a neutral central management. The first chief executive of the NHS, Victor Paige, resigned in frustration at political interference and his lack of room for manoeuvre. (It is important to keep in mind the origins of the Griffiths Inquiry: as a prime ministerially driven attempt to make NHS manpower more accountable, following the 1982 strikes, rather than as a grandiose reorganization only a year after the 1982 change.)

Nevertheless, a whole variety of management initiatives, seeking to build upon the Griffiths changes and increase central control of the Service, while devolving managerial responsibility to some extent, emerged in the 1980s. Following the political embarrassment of leaked documents prior to the 1983 general election, the Conservatives in both the 1983 and 1987 general elections adopted a steady-as-she-goes approach to the Service. It was surprising, therefore, when the Prime Minister's Review of the National Health Service was announced at the beginning of 1988, to even suggest a radical rethink of possibly the essence of the NHS, and even its conceivable replacement by an alternative system such as health insurance or a substantially increased reliance on private care. The reason for the suddenly announced Review was in fact one of the greatest continual problems of the NHS.

Since its earliest days the NHS had encountered problems in meeting demand for health care within limited resources. It is inevitable that most health care systems in the modern world will have the same problem. Whether health care is paid for publicly or privately, and whether it is provided publicly or privately, demands may well outstrip supply. In a public system such as the NHS, however, the effect is much more visible because funds are centrally provided, and it is therefore a central political decision as to what extend demand is met on the one hand, or rationing of care is instituted on the other.

In the US, individuals and firms are much more responsible for health care. It seems there is less rationing there because a lack of ability to pay may well prevent people from registering their demands upon the system. In addition, the US spends considerably more money-per-head on health care than Britain.

The politics of rationing has become an increasingly important issue in the delivery of British health care. The private sector, although it has grown moderately since the election of the Conservative government and various forms of encouragement to the private sector after 1979, has until recently been relatively insignificant in Britain. Only in the area of elective surgery does it play a significant rôle; and only in London is the private sector a weighty partner to the public sector.

Given an NHS which is still in many respects free at the point of use, the rationing of health care is a fundamental political issue in Britain. Whether one's MP is left-wing Labour or right-wing Conservative, when it comes to championing local cottage hospitals in the constituency, it is likely that ideology will be forgotten. The prime minister, as first lord of the treasury, may speak the language of rationalizing the NHS; as an MP, she or he is much more likely to bang the drum to keep open hospitals which have been the subject of political pledges.

The reasons for the debate about health service funding sharpening in recent years are many. Firstly, although most countries in the Western world have seen health expenditures increase significantly in the last few years, Britain's rate of increase has been less than many of its Western companions and competitors. The government is the purchaser which demands health care in Britain, and the government has generally been a mean purchaser. Secondly, it is possible to supply more and more complex health care, which in turn creates demands with significant financial implications as a result of progress in medical technology, and progress in care generally. Thirdly, the inflation which has affected the health care sector in particular, as opposed to the economy as a whole, has been higher in the former than in the latter. As a result, more money in real terms has been necessary to buy health care. Fourthly, and significantly, the demography of the population is affecting demand for health care: as the population ages, elderly cohorts place much more demand for health care, as well as social care generally, on the system. Fifthly, special needs have been identified in recent years – such as Aids – which have huge consequences for health services. Sixthly, the government in Britain, while just about maintaining real expenditure on the NHS, significantly cut spending in other areas of social policy in the 1980s. Local authorities have seen their budgets slashed, including the funds available for housing; and social protection generally has diminished, with the partial exception of the NHS. In consequence, the NHS is having to sweep up much of society's mess.

Examples of this are not hard to find. In London, although there are more hospital beds per thousand population – even when one has controlled for the age and relative sickness of the population – other social services may be too poor and support systems too inadequate to allow early discharge of patients from hospital in line with government directives. Even within the NHS, support to needy general practices in large cities, especially inner cities, may be inadequate, and non-hospital care's inadequacies may mean that hospital is the first port of call for people needing care rather than cure.

Recent health policy debates in Britain at the political level have tended to stress what are known as inputs rather than outputs and outcomes. Inputs are the components required to deliver a service or product – numbers of doctors, amount of money, and so forth. Outputs are the products delivered – numbers of operations, numbers of people treated, and so forth. Outcomes are the most significant measure in the long term: in health care, an outcome might be the health status of the population generally, or its improvement as a result of health-care programmes. A hospital operation may be an output from the health-care system; an outcome, however, would look at the long-term success of that operation in affecting the health of the individual.

The government has paid significant lip-service to the concepts of efficiency and effectiveness. Efficiency measures how well one does something, and effectiveness measures how successfully an aim is achieved. Cost-effectiveness, for example, measures how to achieve a given end with minimum resources, or on the other hand, how to apply set resources to achieve maximum purpose.

In practice, however, the government has encountered political debate about inputs in health care. It has also focused much of its attention on process rather than outcome. Management reforms have been paid more attention than the health care of the population, and, in particular, worrying factors such as once-again-worsening differentials between social classes in health status. Instead, the government has sought to make value-for-money the linchpin of its policy. Yet it is not adequately identified what is to be measured when seeking efficiency, as opposed to rather short-term and mechanistic definitions of cost improvement.

THE MOUNTING FINANCIAL CRISIS

It is an irony that the laudable methodology to allocate resources by admittedly imprecise criteria of need, embraced by the RAWP of 1976, began to be instituted at a time of a general financial crisis for the British government. Redistribution of resources from one area of the country to another will always be more palatable if it takes place in the overall context of growth; losers then are only losers in a relative sense if everyone is gaining just by different degrees. The mid-1970s, however, saw a significant slowdown in growth in social spending generally, including the NHS. As a result, although expenditure was maintained in real terms, always with the proviso that increases were significantly less than in other comparable countries, a policy of redistribution of resources very crudely from the south-east to the north-west of England, and with analogous changes in the other countries of the United Kingdom, meant that areas losing money were running into serious problems.

The formula allocated resources on the basis of population weighted by its age and sex breakdown – for example, older populations would be a higher target for allocation of resources – and also by morbidity as measured by death rates. In practice this meant that as well as the broad drift of money from the south-east to the north-west, redistributions within regions became critical. While the national operation of the formula was dealing with populations large enough for problems to average out to some extent, the allocation of money within, for example, the four Thames Regions, within the West Midlands Region and within the Mersey Region, were causing significant problems. Inner-city areas, for example, may be losing populations yet might still be operating in a context of significant social deprivation as well as maintaining expensive and prestigious centres of excellence, namely large teaching hospitals. Professor Alain Enthoven, who published his reflections of the management of the NHS in 1985, and was one of the leading intellectual gurus underpinning the analysis of the Prime Minister's Review, observed in 1984 that Guy's Hospital was being ground down by the operation of RAWP. It was at the sub-regional, rather than the national, level that RAWP was causing significant problems.

Often the overall level of funding going to the health service did not exactly help. In areas of the country such as London, which had always been used to higher quantities and levels of service, removing them was bound to cause more overt problems than continuing to deny them in areas which had never had them, which expected them less, and which often made less noise about the problem. Nevertheless, the political manifestations of the crisis lay in familiar newspaper headlines and news bulletin reports about closed wards, waiting-lists, and the denial of care to individuals.

In 1985, the Minister of State for Health, Barney Hayhoe – with a sensitive London constituency – was experiencing the problem at a personal level. Hence, there were political as well as academic motivations behind an attempt to improve the resource allocation methodology, represented by the establishment of a team to review the RAWP formula, which produced an interim report in December 1986 and a final report at the end of July 1988. The essential political import of the new recommendations was to repatriate some of the money back to London and the south-east.

In the interim, however, the Conservatives had won the general election of 1987 by another landslide in terms of seats won, and the political pressure had lifted somewhat. Not long after this election victory, with the advent of winter 1987, the whole debate began again in a more acute form. An alleged crisis at a children's unit in Birmingham gained much media attention, and the symptoms of the overall problem were the now-familiar temporary and permanent closures of wards due to financial and staff shortages.

Associated with the disquiet about health-service funding as it affected acute services, was concern that priorities which had been identified for the 1970s onwards in areas of chronic and community care were not being addressed due to shortages of funds. Worries about the future of medical research, and the longer-term implications for important current specialties like neonatal care and developing specialties also surfaced at this time.

An important factor in the increasing frustration within the NHS at government policy was that what often seemed an unnecessarily restrictive policy of funding was accompanied by shortsightedness and inconsistency in planning. Here, however, it should be noted that even planning in a very basic sense was rendered difficult by the government's behaviour. Planning at its most general may be considered to be the choice of priorities and the identification of routes to achieving these. Long-term financial planning was impossible in the NHS in the 1980s due to sudden and abrupt financial and manpower cuts, as in 1983, and also sudden increases, announced separately from the Budget statement. The government's unacknowledged pay policy for the public sector was compounded by under-funded wage and salary increases for NHS workers, which put unpredictable pressure upon health services' priority developments.

Prior to the announcement of the Prime Minister's Review in 1988, government responses to anxiety about general health service underfunding had been cosmetic, as in the waiting-list initiative of 1987. The announcement of the Review represented a radical new strategy, as we shall see.

Chapter Three

Ideology, right-wing ideas, and Conservative reforms: the Prime Minister's Review

THE SEEDS OF A RADICAL CONSERVATIVE RESPONSE

It was as a result of the increasing dissatisfaction with levels of funding – and therefore levels of service and inequality of access – that alternatives to the NHS model began to have more currency. It had always been a small, right-wing and libertarian minority which had opposed the principles underpinning a publicly funded, publicly provided NHS. They had, however, been firmly out in the political cold, as had much of the Thatcherite wing of the Conservative party prior to the defeat of Edward Heath in 1975. There were fundamentally three options from which a right-wing attack on the principles of the NHS could choose.

Firstly, removing universal public financing could lead to private financing, with possibly public insurance for the poorest in society, to be combined with privatized, or at least no longer state-owned, hospitals on the provision side: thorough-going privatization could occur. Secondly, significant user charges, meaning payments by the patient, could be instituted, ending the principle of the NHS as a free service. Thirdly, while public financing and even central financing could be retained, hospitals and providing units could be privatized or floated off such that provision, unlike financing, was no longer public. Options such as these were explored in the early days of the Prime Minister's Review.

Certain right-wing or pro-market critiques of the NHS pointed not so much to the fact that it was inefficient and therefore by implication too expensive, but to the fact that it did not allow enough to be spent on health care. This inverted the left's argument that other countries spent more and therefore more should be spent on the NHS. The right-wing version of this argument was that it was only in countries where health care was not provided through a national health service that more could be spent, as it was only in such systems that a plural system of financing, depending upon individual employer and state contributions to insurance policies, could ensure a higher level of spending. Both emphases – that the NHS spent too much and too little – stressed the 'arbitrariness' of a system in which individuals did not trade off the benefits of health care against the costs of private purchasers.

As in other areas of social spending, a significant plank of the Conservative argument has been that people will not finance the same level of expenditure on services from general taxation as they will spend directly on themselves. Individualist ideology is adopted by the right-winger in this type of argument. Such a perspective, of course, ignores the possibility that collectivized or socialized services may be more efficient, not less so. The overwhelming evidence concerning the NHS is that it is more efficient, and indeed in many cases more effective as well, than other systems. If this is the case, then the Conservative argument for individualism in health care is either misconceived or beholden to a hidden agenda.

That hidden agenda is perhaps the unwillingness of the better-off to redistribute through the tax system and effectively subsidize poorer people's health care. If individualism is taken to its nineteenth-century extreme, then there may indeed be an argument for the privileged to oppose the NHS. However, given the sharp decline in the progressiveness of the tax system following the Chancellor's budgets of the late 1980s, even this stance is less tenable than before. There is a good case that all individuals in the country can obtain better financial value from the NHS than from an alternative. Even in conditions of financial stringency, the NHS has continued to provide high-quality medical care, except where closures have literally denied particular services. It is the hotel-side of the business which has suffered most severely in terms of reputation, in an age when the population expects more than a no-frills service.

THE PRELUDE TO RIGHT-WING REFORMS

In 1979, Margaret Thatcher came to power as Prime Minister and at the time of writing, Britain has seen well over a decade of Conservative government. Whether or not there has been an attack on the welfare state, there is widespread agreement that the welfare state has been restructured (Taylor-Gooby, 1985). Until the end of 1987, it was not thought likely that the NHS would be restructured significantly, to accompany other changes in social policy. There are a number of reasons for this. It is one of the country's most popular institutions, as consistently borne out by opinion polling (MORI/Nuffield Provincial Hospitals Trust, 1985); only recently have shortages begun to affect attitudes to parts of the Service. A national health services model of financing and providing health care is considered to be both equitable and economical. The government had no coherent idea of how to proceed with any radical reform, even were this desirable.

The essence of the NHS is that it is both publicly financed and, in the main, publicly provided. Public finance, mainly through direct taxation, allows central control of overall resources going to the Service. Public provision allows, in theory at least, resource allocation to regions, and below regions to be linked to plans for provision of facilities.

Earlier in the lifetime of the post-1979 Conservative administrations, there has been interest shown in moving away from one or both of these principles. In the first Thatcher administration, the Secretary of State for Social Services, Patrick Jenkin, commissioned studies of alternative modes of financing and providing health care in Britain. In particular, he showed interest in lessons from the US and France. The tacit hypothesis at this stage was that a move to a system of national health insurance was being contemplated; since the aim was greater rather than less cost control, this idea was abandoned in 1982, by which time Norman Fowler had replaced Jenkin. Authoritative and politically neutral comparison such as that being developed for the Nuffield Trust publication *The Public/Private Mix for Health* (McLachlan and Maynard, 1982) had some influence in leading to its abandonment. Were a greater percentage of GDP to be desired for health care, moving to the American system might make sense, with the proviso that more of the financing would be private. This, however, was not the government's aim; quite the reverse.

The rhetorical claim that 'The NHS is safe in our hands' dominated Conservative statements between 1983–7, embracing the general election of the latter year. Despite difficulties caused by the level of overall finance, and the fact that redistribution through the RAWP formula was affecting in particular inner cities and teaching hospitals, the crisis had not yet hit, as it did later in 1987, and particularly early in 1988.

Nothing dramatic had suddenly happened, only that both objective events and a media bandwagon was bringing home the nature of the crisis to the public in an ever more concentrated form. Ironically, spending on the NHS is the one area of social policy where Conservative government behaviour did not differ substantially from what might have been expected from a government of another political party. Despite the government's boast of the 1987 election of an increase in spending in real terms between 1979–87 of 27%, the reality was somewhat different. A number of factors limited the salience of this statistic, but in particular, demographic change; technological advance; and 'extra' health-service inflation.

The fact that the RAWP (DHSS, 1976b; NHS Management Board, 1988) was redistributing resources broadly from south to north, and from cities to suburbs, meant that closures in children's wards, cancer wards, and intensive care wards in London and Birmingham hit the headlines.

The fact that other districts and regions in the country have expanded services (which they had never had) has often been ignored, and admittedly limited in its overall effect by the tight control of the NHS budget.

It is possible that, without any evidence of its greater efficiency (quite the reverse), the government was attempting to promote both the provision of private care and access to private care.

The crisis, partly real, partly media-led, 'hit'. The government sought to seize the initiative by directing the debate from one about financing to one about provision and reform and instituted an internal review geared to exploring all possible options for restructuring or replacement of the NHS. The Prime Minister, say supporters and contributors to the review, was not intrinsically hostile to the NHS, but was frustrated at receiving increasing abuse in proportion to what she saw as increasing financial commitment to the NHS. Agreeing implicitly with the former Conservative Minister of Health, Enoch Powell's earlier warning, she saw the NHS's constituent professions as having a vested interest in denigrating the Service – to get more money.

The review was to investigate ways of seeing tangible value for money. The Prime Minister saw the NHS as a black hole swallowing funds without trace or evidence of result. Although there was no immediate plan or conspiracy to dismantle the NHS, the government hoped to turn the crisis of under-funding in the opposite direction to that intended by those who plead most regularly that the NHS is under-funded.

The argument became that if a health system almost wholly funded from the public purse cannot satisfy its critics, an alternative must be found. This is of course a great irony. Not only was Britain spending a lower percentage of its GDP on total health care than nearly all its competitors, but it was spending a lower percentage of the GDP on public health provision, i.e. on the NHS, than those countries, with the exception of the US.

ALTERNATIVE DIRECTIONS

The main advocacy for a full privatization model, involving privatization of financing of health care as well as the provision of health care, came from the Institute of Economic Affairs Health Unit, a component of a right-wing think-tank, whose director was Dr David Green. However, the political costs as well as the financial costs of a privatization of the sort advocated would be high indeed.

The second major option – moving towards the introduction of significant user charges in health care while maintaining a publicly provided national health service – was also likely to be very politically unpopular. Naturally, the public, Conservative as well as Labour, would be set against it. Furthermore, pro-competitive ideologists such as John Redwood, now Conservative MP for Wokingham, a former Head of the Prime Minister's No. 10 Policy Unit (Willetts, 1987) and a frequent pamphleteer on health during the Prime Minister's Review (Redwood, 1988; Redwood and Letwin, 1988), opposed the idea of what they saw as a monopolistic, publicly owned service, charging its choiceless customers. After all, a pro-market ideology would call for competing suppliers to benefit the consumer, not a monopoly supplier holding the consumer to ransom. There were of course those who saw such a policy as being a vast encouragement to the private sector: after all, if one is having to pay for health care anyway, why not pay for personalized health care in the private sector?

The third overall direction identified – preserving public financing yet seeking competition in supply – gradually gained the upper hand during the Prime Minister's Review.

A disturbing aspect of the Review was that the terms of its debate were set by individuals with little experience in health policy and management. This does not exclude them on the grounds of intelligence, but it did raise doubts about their suitability for conducting a detailed Review about a complex service. The wisdom of the Review was questioned by many close to the Prime Minister. The already massive managerial and structural changes set in train by the development of general management, if compounded by significant changes in the financing and provision of health services, would it seemed, render the Service ungovernable.

More worrying was that the interesting potential in the NHS for the fruitful reconciliation of resource allocation and planning to meet need could be threatened by policies which fragmented either financing or planned provision. This is not to idealize existing procedures. However, there are many promising aspects of NHS planning and resource allocation as it has been evolving which can be improved by refinements in policy. Many of the stated objectives of the Review could be met in a different political and policy context.

What has been described as the silly season of pamphleteering dominated the early stages of the Review. Treating such proposals analytically rather than descriptively, they fell into the following categories:

Firstly, there were proposals to end the NHS, move to a system of health insurance, and return responsibility for buying care or insurance to the individual. These proposals were not new, and would have led to more expensive, less efficient, and less equitable health care. They were advocated most prominently by the Health Unit of the Institute of Economic Affairs (Green, 1986; Green, 1988), a formerly peripheral body which now found itself thrust to centre stage. John Redwood, former Head of the No. 10 Policy Unit, has also advocated *inter alia* radical privatization (Redwood and Letwin, 1988). Minor or less radical versions of this proposal exist, and include the significant extension of tax credits for private insurance. This would be grossly inequitable: pressure for even lower taxes would stem from the acquired habit of purchasing expensive private care, and would undermine even the rump NHS left behind. A two-tier service would be even more pronounced than is often predicted. That is why this idea was so disturbing.

Secondly, there was the proposal advocated in a number of policy areas, including education, to give health vouchers to individuals to buy care where they please, supplemented perhaps by private funds. This proposal could, if necessary, be combined with the third or fourth points below. Vouchers could mean privatization of financing, as with the above, or a retention of public financing, or a mixture.

Thirdly, there were proposals to float off the hospital sector and replace districts, as currently known, with health management units (HMUs), which would contract for care with public (now voluntary?) and private hospitals. While ingeniously propounded by the Adam Smith Institute (Butler and Pirie, 1988) and others, the idea would, in practice, be difficult to arrange. It was a classic result of think-tank-based academics burning the midnight oil to devise policy from abstract ideology, in this case, competitive supply. GPs would be associated through a contract with particular HMUs. Individuals might be able to choose which HMU to join, but referrals to hospitals by GPs would be controlled by the terms of their contracts with HMUs, acting like American HMOs.

This leads to consideration of the fourth proposal, to give budgets to GPs, who would then buy in care for their patients from the hospital and other sectors. The efficient and effective would allegedly prosper. The idea was adapted from the variant of the American HMO, which gives the primary decision-making rôle to a primary physician gatekeeper, who controls access to more expensive, specialized care and prevents unnecessary use. Professor Alan Maynard of York University was associated with this idea, but saw it as just that: not a finalized policy proposal (Bevan *et al.*, 1988).

As we move to the less-drastic proposals, we find they tended to advocate retaining public finance, but encouraging more private provision. They also tended to retain the health authority rather than the individual as the direct purchaser of health care.

The best-known proposal in this category was that of the internal market, proposed by Professor Alain Enthoven in his 1985 publication for the Nuffield Provincial Hospitals Trust (Enthoven, 1985). Dr David Owen's interest in this proposal, announced at the Institute of Health Services Management Conference at Coventry in 1985 (Owen, 1985), predated the Prime Minister's growing attraction to it by a number of years, let alone months. It was always likely to be a Tory policy, however, given its stress on markets. It tended to be viewed suspiciously by Labour due to its associations with the government after meetings of the No. 10 policy unit and editorial writers close to the Conservatives had embraced it, placing it alongside more partisan policies. Enthoven, while a pro-competitive analyst, was not intrinsically hostile to the NHS or a politically partisan actor in a British context. Indeed, to make the notion of the internal market more attractive to defenders of the NHS, it was briefly described as 'market socialism'.

The internal market, although better known as a theoretical slogan than as a practical proposal, would mean districts trading with each other to provide and consume care, with the rôles of GP referrals and patient sovereignty unclear. It was at first suggested that the idea be introduced as a pilot project, although cross-charging between authorities existed already in an *ad hoc* manner in the NHS.

It does not entail by necessity any private provision, but was associated by a Conservative government with greater private provision, whether of clinical or support services. This would entail a full or external market, not an internal market composed of public providers within the NHS.

There is an approximate continuum, in this admittedly brief sketch, which runs from radical to less radical, in that, for example, the fifth category would retain a system like RAWP in making allocations to districts. But the beneficial rôle of regions, whether current or potential, in strategically planning services and gearing them to equity and need in a wide catchment area, would be lost. The fourth through to the first would in varying degrees lose the major benefits of resources distributed to populations, with risks thereby spread, and planning made more coherent.

The major advantage of the NHS is its capacity for need-based planning. Many contributors to the Review advocated the abolition of regions, but, if implemented, this superficially popular anti-bureaucratic view would lead to administrative costs and tangles which would be much worse. Commentators who wished to abolish regions were not aware of their potential for planning strategically, and ensuring that reward related to workload for hospitals and units throughout the region. A major aim of the Review was to relate financial reward to workload for providers. But radical schemes such as self-governing hospitals were not necessary to achieve this. Furthermore, abolishing regions would abolish the institution which could manage a competitive strategy to achieve this. None of the self-appointed experts dominating the Review seemed even to be aware of how to determine factors such as supra-district specialties; practical criteria for trading and pricing between districts; and modelling equitable flows of patients to enable equality of opportunity of access.

The Review represented the heyday of Prime Ministerial government, when both the Cabinet and government departments were marginalized. The Prime Minister relied heavily on advice from favoured outsiders. This state of affairs was partly reversed under John Major.

A large-scale conspiracy theory concerning the government's intention to downgrade the NHS was probably less convincing than a scenario which viewed the think-tankers opportunistically filling a vacuum, and ironically benefiting from public concern at the funding of the NHS. However, there were more radical ideas than radical thinkers floating around; we seemed to be witnessing the market principle undergoing a *reductio ad absurdum*, whereby alternative and inconsistent schemes were floated to see which would sell. The tracts were not weighty, but the NHS was in danger of being weighed down by their implications. The heyday of the Review represented the radical chic of the right-wing applied to health policy.

The main reform proposals which consciously built on the ideas of Enthoven came from the right-wing of politics. This was itself an irony: although Enthoven has in some circles in Britain a reputation for being a right-winger, it is only his belief in the competitive market which justifies this. In the US, although his ideas were enthusiastically expounded by the Reagan administration, he is one of the foremost advocates of fairer access to the system by the poor, by the ending of over-generous tax credits for health care to the well-off, and the redistribution of this money to the currently uninsured and under-served poor and minorities. It was the right-wingers, however, who made the running, given that the left found itself understandably in a conservative role – defending the NHS from its opponents. When the radical right had been marginalized in the 1960s and 1970s, it had been safer to criticize the NHS – from a left-wing viewpoint. But now such behaviour could be destabilizing, to the advantage of the right.

There were also proposals before the Review to change the system of finance for the NHS without removing its public nature. Both Conservative and Labour politicians made these proposals: the former Conservative Home Secretary, Leon Brittan, advocated that a special health tax incorporating national insurance, thus promoting a compromise between the NHS model and a National Health Insurance, be adopted in Britain; Frank Field, Labour MP and the new Chairman of the Social Services Select Committee, advocated a similar proposal – although with less scope for private additions to public finance and less implication of private provision of care than in the Brittan proposal (Brittan, 1988;

Field, 1988). John Moore, the Secretary of State in 1988 had an interest in tax credits for private health care to be extended beyond the current income limit of £8,500 a year. The 1980 limit, since unadjusted, was proposed at the time as the best way of persuading amenable trade unions to enrol members. In the end, the Electrical, Electronic, Telecommunications and Plumbing Union (EETPU) was the main union so to do.

THE STRUCTURE OF THE PRIME MINISTER'S REVIEW

The Prime Minister's Review, announced in January 1988, was so called because the Prime Minister announced a fundamental review into the future of the NHS in response to questions on the television programme 'Panorama', unknown in advance by Ministers, civil servants, or the Conservative Party.

The Review process continued a trend in the Conservative administration of bypassing traditional policy-making bodies or investigatory mechanisms. Instead of Departmental officials from the policy divisions of the Department of Health as well as the permanent secretary and others at the top of the office constituting the key personnel in the Review, informal deliberations constituted the key sessions of the process, which were attended in the early stages by the Prime Minister and throughout by more informal advisers such as those in the No. 10 Policy Unit, former members of that unit, and members of think-tanks – the Centre for Policy Studies in particular, but also the Adam Smith Institute, and, in the early days, the Institute of Economic Affairs Health Unit, before its prescriptions for dismembering the NHS's public financing system fell foul of an emerging pragmatism.

The Review Committee was formally chaired by the Prime Minister. Its other members were: Chancellor of the Exchequer, Nigel Lawson; Chief Secretary to the Treasury, John Major; Secretaries of State for Scotland and Wales, Malcolm Rifkind and Peter Walker; and Social Services Secretary and Minister of Health, John Moore and Tony Newton – the former later replaced by Health Secretary, Kenneth Clarke when the Department was split at the end of July 1988. The civil servant leading the Secretariat was Strachan Heppel, deputy secretary in social security. Economic advisers, permanent and seconded, in the Department also contributed. There was no consultation on a formal basis with the British Medical Association, the Royal Colleges of medicine, other health care professions' official bodies, or the public. Invited contributions on an *ad hoc* basis from academics and others were considered.

The Review originally was to report by the summer of 1988, but dispute over policy and difficulty in devising practical reform proposals prolonged its deliberations until early 1989, with the publication of the White Paper.

The Review Committee met weekly, with limited contributions from private health-care executives, businessmen, including Sir Roy Griffiths, at this time deputy chairman of the NHS management board and the PM's personal adviser, and generalists from the policy community on the right wing of politics.

In the end, the Review adopted the core idea of provider markets within the NHS in an attempt to maintain public financing yet escape the bureaucratic system of planned provision. Some of the more right-wing advisers saw the Review's conclusions as a half-way house to more thoroughgoing privatization in a fourth Conservative term. The Prime Minister saw the NHS as a 'black hole', swallowing up resources without trace; while she was not hostile *per se* to public spending on it, it perhaps seemed that putting in more money led to more, not less, criticism and continuing complaints of cuts. Measuring outputs and outcomes in health care was her unstated objective, as well as a concern for value for money. Naturally, her opponents saw it differently.

THE STAGES OF THE PM'S REVIEW

It is important to remember the background to the Review. Growing concern, expressed especially in 1985 and again towards the end of 1987, about under-funding of the NHS was occasioned by crises in large teaching hospitals, in London and Birmingham especially. The government felt increasingly on the defensive about the politics and financing of the NHS. The Prime Minister decided to move on to the offensive, and announced a fundamental review into the future of the NHS at the beginning of 1988. The skill lay in transforming what had been a debate about whether funding was adequate or not into a debate about the nature of the delivery of health care. The Review's conclusions were published on 1 February 1989 as the White Paper *Working for Patients*. By then the debate had been transformed from one about the demand, or financing side, of health care into one about the efficient delivery of health care through provider markets.

How did this come about? Let us consider the evolution of the Review. Apart from a brief investigation in 1981–2 of alternative systems of financing for health care, it was the first time since the introduction of the NHS in 1948 that radical alternatives to funding health care were being seriously considered in Britain.

The Secretary of State from 1987–8, John Moore, was keen to examine alternative systems of financing: principally, various health insurance models ranging from National Health Insurance, publicly funded in the main, through to various alternatives in the realm of private insurance; vouchers earmarked for health care; and significant tax relief for private insurance.

The first stage of the Review led to much pamphleteering by think-tanks such as the Institute of Economic Health Unit, the Centre for Policy Studies, and the Adam Smith Institute (Green, 1988; Willetts and Goldsmith, 1988; Redwood, 1988; Redwood and Letwin, 1988; Butler and Pirie, 1988). These proposals were very general and concerned both the financing and provision of health care. In the end, Moore personally chose the option of a financing initiative, allowing individuals to contract-out of the NHS on the analogy of contracting-out of state pensions, a policy with which Strachan Heppel, deputy secretary in the DHSS heading the administration of the Review, was identified. But such options were anathema to the Treasury as they meant unnecessary tax relief to those already with private insurance, and, more importantly, the loss of direct revenue on a large scale, and politically very risky.

Even Mrs Thatcher felt she could not move against the NHS, and her personal advisers felt that the radical policy agenda for the third term of office, including the controversial poll-tax and various contentious privatizations, was already taking its toll on government energy and taxing public patience.

Given the deep political unpopularity of radical moves away from a tax-funded NHS, there was difficulty in designing proposals compatible with a radical review of the NHS within the bounds of political pragmatism. The Prime Minister's dissatisfaction with Moore's radical yet impractical proposals on the financing side, yet absence of ideas concerning the provision of health care on the supply side, led to his dismissal in July 1988 from the Department of Health half of his job, and later to complete dismissal in 1989. The Department was now split into two departments, health and social security.

Phase two of the Review was marked by consolidation by the new Secretary of State for Health, Kenneth Clarke, formerly Minister of State in the Department from 1982–85. Clarke, a supporter of the NHS when set against many of his more sceptical Conservative colleagues, was thought likely to abandon radical ideas altogether and to go further down the road of efficient public management, as represented by the Griffiths Inquiry in 1983 (Griffiths, 1983) with which he (rather than the Secretary of State at the time, Norman Fowler) had been particularly identified. Thus, it was likely that existing initiatives for better management of public money, such as resource management, and measures such as clinical audit, would be continued and beefed up. It was further thought that, as well as forcing doctors to take responsibility for speciality and departmental budgets in order to husband resources better, Clarke might seek to put NHS clinicians on short-term contracts in return for higher salaries. The rationale for this would be to make consultants more accountable to health authority priorities.

The Review entered phase three when the Prime Minister's dissatisfaction with the lack of a radical agenda led to the adoption of radical ideas on the supply-side of health care. The concept of provider markets, a broader version of Enthoven's concept of the internal market, became the linchpin of the Review. Other less radical components of the Review included further moves to medical audit, and the control of family practitioner services. The move to a corporate management model for health care also was enhanced, as the NHS supervisory board, now wholly defunct, and the NHS management board were replaced with, respectively, an NHS policy board, composed primarily of Ministers and businessmen, and an NHS executive, to be responsible for implementation of ministerial strategy (Department of Health, 1989a).

It is possible to separate the management initiatives from the political, pro-market components of the Review. If the latter are diminished in import over time, the essence of the Review may be seen to be a further move to tighter management, tighter control of doctors and workers, and more rigid contracting for services from providers. Along with this goes the more traditional civil service agenda of greater audit. There were signs by 1990 that damage limitation required less emphasis on competitive markets and more on control by regions, and the NHS management executive, of how quickly the new purchasers and providers could move. Regulation in the name of accountability to Parliament, and in particular the Public Accounts Committee, meant limitations on room for manoeuvre by free providers.

THE GRIFFITHS REPORT

The Griffiths Report 1983 had set out a blueprint which would take politics out of the NHS and provide a corporate management board, as in nationalized industries. The aim was that management could be left to manage. However, as the first chief executive and chairman of the NHS management board, Victor Paige, pointed out on resigning in frustration, this was never politically realistic.

The White Paper arrangements centralized political control and made NHS management, from the new management executive through to the more tightly managed regional and district health authorities, more likely to act at the behest of political priorities. A likely consequence of the White Paper's implementation was that political intervention in health care became more direct rather than less obtrusive, albeit in the context of a corporate management structure. Already, by the end of 1989, the ambulance dispute suggested that the NHS management executive was likely to act as a conduit for political directives, rather than as an autonomous management board.

These developments were an attempt to clear up some inconsistencies in the pre-White-Paper NHS. A problem with the half-way house of the Griffiths Report had been that the new managerial line of control from the secretary of state and the NHS management board, through to regional and district general managers had cut across other lines of control. The secretary of state also was at the top of a line linking regional chairmen and regional health authorities with district chairmen and district health authorities. The chief medical officer was the head of a medical line of control through regional down to district medical officers. A consequence of the 1989 White Paper was to diminish lines of control other than the key political/managerial one. Health authorities were no longer to be quasi-independent, drawing members from professional groups, public interest groups, trade unions, and the public at large. Instead, they were to be effectively corporate boards.

Thus, health authorities would no longer be loosely representative bodies rooted in their communities, but mere adjuncts to their local management boards. Alternative sources of advice to the Department of Health, whether through lay authorities or through the medical professions, were to be subjugated to the new structures, entrenching general management, which established firm lines of control from the top down. The irony here is that political unpopularity deriving from rationalizing measures, such as hospital closures, was not deflected to the locally responsible managers, as Ministers hoped, but channelled upwards to Ministers, who were no longer protected by independent-minded health authorities.

A publicly funded NHS, whether or not services are publicly provided, is bound to be scrutinized by Parliament and government. The difficulty in devising a management board which was allegedly to be independent of the Department of Health in the original Griffiths Report, was that parliamentary and government oversight might be reduced. Ministers were never likely to loosen the reins to this extent: otherwise, they would be left with responsibility without power to act.

The White Paper's attempts at furthering the general management of the NHS lay in a different direction. They accepted political control, and accepted that the new policy board would be dominated by politicians as well as industrialists. The management executive would be the management arm for the policy board, shorn of the pretensions which the original NHS management board originally had, and the absence of which in practice led to the resignation of Victor Paige in 1986, that it would be independent, rather like the board of a fairly autonomous public corporation.

In his Rock Carling monograph, Sir Kenneth Stowe, former permanent secretary of the DHSS, argued that most change in the NHS has foundered on the rocks of the need for public monitoring and public control, whether by the Public Accounts Committee, whether indirectly in recent years by the social services select committee, or, indeed, whether by the Health Services Commissioner, the ombudsman. (Stowe, 1988)

THE CONTENTS OF THE WHITE PAPER

The eight Working Papers which followed the White Paper after two weeks did not provide much more detail than the Paper itself. The key themes of the White Paper are reflected in the titles of the Working Papers, which are only marginally amended in the following list, of which the first three are the most radical and crucial.

1. Self-Governing Hospitals
2. Funding and Contracts for Hospital Services
3. Practice Budgets for GPs
4. Indicative Prescribing Budgets for GPs
5. Capital Charges
6. Medical Audit
7. NHS Consultants: Appointments, Contracts, and Awards
8. Implications for Family Practitioner Committees
(Department of Health, 1989b)

Self-Governing Hospitals

The most plausible rationale for self-governing hospitals is to free up providing institutions to compete as flexible actors in the marketplace. For the purposes of this theory, hospitals are to include all forms of health care. Secretary of State Kenneth Clarke announced later in 1989, under some pressure, that community units, or parts of them , would also be allowed to opt-out. As in education, the ideology argues that independent institutions are more able to set their own objectives and to manage their own resources and then make themselves appealing to the client, whether this is the parent, in education, or the sick person's advocate, in the NHS – the health manager acting as purchaser of health care.

The irony is that where competition looked likely to work and to force closures in, say, London, the government halted trust status for hospitals seeking it in October 1991 in order to set up the Tomlinson Commission to plan London's future. Only where trusts could be guaranteed survival were they allowed.

Contracting for Services

Funding and provision are now, in theory, separated. The district is the purchaser, having been given funds by the Department of Health via the region. Contracts with providers, whether self-governing hospitals and units, or directly managed units, are made by the district, which determines the mix of services to be provided. This allows the district, in theory, to promote clarity of thought in determining its care mix, and certainly does not involve a priori any diminution of the claims of priority groups such as the elderly, chronically and mentally ill, and of, for example, community care.

In practice, however, this measure may have robbed the NHS of a considerable amount of flexibility. For the difficulties inherent in predicting and costing need for health care, when quantified by a system of contracts, have produced a more bureaucratic and regulated NHS than existed prior to the White Paper. Districts are the purchasers of health care for their residents. Thus, patients and GPs have their preferences subjugated to those of managers.

Pre-White Paper, GP referral was not controlled, even if the money did not always follow the patient quickly because of the operation of the resource-allocation formula. Post-White Paper, although the money follows the patient, with units paid in proportion to their workload, referrals are rationed. This will be done rationally in the eyes of the White Paper's defenders, by managers. The age of a rationed NHS, long existing informally, has formally dawned. Waiting-lists are the responsibility of the purchaser in such a system. It is politically convenient to cut waiting-lists simply by not allowing people on to them. Pretending that rationing can be done by scientific criteria which are both intellectually robust and morally acceptable, or either, is a deceit.

The main problem is that districts are in fact both purchasers and providers. A real marketplace in provision cannot be established for this reason, and also because regions and districts need to have some certainty as to where patients will be treated in order to provide resources accordingly.

The policy of charging for capital (Department of Health, 1989b) meant logically that regions would be the banker which provides hospitals and units with capital or denies them. Capital charging is intended to ensure that prices of services reflect capital costs – depreciation and rental of capital, on accounting principles – that is, that costs are global, as in the private sector, where any purchase generally reflects the total cost of production and not just the running costs. Making the region the disburser of capital, on the provision side, was thought necessary, since the district was the purchaser on the demand side. The rôles of purchaser and provider were already confused, or inadequately separated. This confusion could not be accentuated by making the district the disburser of capital to providing units as well as purchaser from them, but making the region the banker gave it a significant, if back-door, planning rôle.

In the future, therefore, regions and districts will effectively be planning services in an even more top-heavy manner than before. The rhetoric is competition; the reality is bureaucratic planning, with the language of contracts and management competition to make it respectable in the eyes of a government to which planning is a dirty word.

GP Budgets for Hospital Care

The intention behind offering practice budgets to those GP practices with populations greater than 11,000, and with an ability to demonstrate the capacity to manage their own budgets for certain defined aspects of hospital care, was to provide a rival purchaser to the district health authority, and to make providers more conscious of the need to sell themselves to purchasers. Since GP practices which opt-out are to be funded directly by the region, any resulting shortfall in regional monies for districts will have to be spread over hospitals and units, which in turn will have to sell themselves to the general practices.

In practice, it has proved a very difficult task to find an equitable and yet manageable formula by which GPs' populations' needs could be gauged. The government wanted to avoid the alleged rigidities of the RAWP, used up to 1990 for hospital and community services, and its White Paper successor formula, but has become committed to even more miniscule calculations. District purchasers have faced great financial difficulty as a result of GPs being given budgets based on the actual costs of services. This leaves districts' allocations less generously funded, from cash-limited capitation unrelated to the actual costs of purchasing needed services. This discrepancy is but one of many resulting from ill-thought-out policy. Moreover, allocating to smaller catchment populations in GP practices further diminishes the broad advantages of the NHS system of resource allocation and planning which brought with it an ability to spread risk over large catchment areas, plan services accordingly, and respond to unexpected need relatively flexibly. In 1990 and 1991, the government allowed even smaller practices to be fundholders, and extended the range of services covered to community services in February 1992.

Even more significantly, priorities set by GPs – often under pressure from patients reading glossy magazines on the latest techniques – may diverge from the district health authority's priorities. This would undermine a defence of the White Paper as leading to global needs assessment by an expert purchaser.

IMPLEMENTATION

The problem was that the Department of Health defined the success of the White Paper in terms of process – how many hospitals opt-out;

how contracts are drawn up – rather than outcomes defined by the criterion of how far the health status of a target population is improved.

A major danger is that regulating competition is a much more bureaucratic and cumbersome exercise than merely running a planned public health service. This may go against the prevailing political rhetoric, but is a lesson which we would do well to absorb from the US. Protecting the needs of untrendy local services and poorer local populations and groups is a major challenge following the Review and White Paper.

The internal market was originally suggested by Enthoven as a means of solving the problems faced by large teaching hospitals which were losing money under the RAWP formula: gaining districts (purchasers) outside London could buy services from losing districts' hospitals, allowing, for example, London teaching hospitals to be rewarded for work done for other districts. The essence of Enthoven's idea was to ensure that workload was adequately rewarded. The RAWP formula had in fact sought to provide funds to compensate districts for work done for other districts. Indeed, in certain circumstances it could benefit districts' targets, if not their current allocation, to concentrate on work for other districts. For such cross-boundary flows were costed at national average cost, and if a district's target for its residents was low, then this might be a good way in theory of boosting targets. The problem was that it was only a possibly far-off target that benefited, not current allocation. Furthermore, if district A benefited by having its target so adjusted for treating district B's residents, district B could continue what would become a beggar-my-neighbour policy by treating A's patients. Additionally, poor costing meant that districts could not know if particular referred patients would cost more or less their average costs, even if GPs and hospital doctors were willing to implement theoretical management games!

The formula reimbursed districts for work for other districts only indirectly and slowly. Ironically, given its origins in helping London by allowing its hospitals to charge, the White Paper may now herald the closure of expensive London services, other than those in self-governing hospitals, and a move of provision to the provinces which was ironically never achieved by direct planning in the 1960s and 1970s. This is because districts outside London may eschew London's services on the grounds of cost. Enthoven's assumption that the quality of services in London would save them may not be realized.

Progressing by means of pilot projects was advocated by Enthoven, and this advice was not taken by the government. In defence of the government at the time, it can be argued that the opting-out of hospitals, which occurs gradually, and the gradual evolution of practice budgets for some general practices, in effect takes the form of pilot projects. However, the political need to make things succeed prevented scientific assessment of developments, as extra money was pumped in to prevent the failure of showpiece initiatives such as new self-governing trust hospitals and GP fundholders. Political pressure ensured that interest was expressed in becoming a trust, without intellectual or analytical consideration, by widespread hospitals and units. The fragmentation of formerly united hospital and community units was accepted at a stroke, reversing years of slow but fruitful planning. Devolution in itself is not necessarily a virtue.

In some cases, GPs and health authority management have to make decisions as to priorities. Reconciling the decision of GPs with the decision of authorities was a major challenge facing the White Paper's implementation. *Working for Patients* may be an appropriate title for the White Paper, then, since we are not talking of direct, individual, consumer sovereignty by the patient. Rather, definition of the needs of patients has to be made through consensus between doctors, managers, and health authorities – naturally dependent, at the end of the day, on the government in a centrally funded system.

The rationing of health care at the point of purchase by a global purchaser, rather than allowing rationing to be done informally by providers of care, is the key theme of the White Paper. However, the status of the district health authority as a monopsonistic public purchaser, was diluted by giving optional budgets to GPs for certain categories of non-immediate hospital care. This policy was opposed by many involved in the NHS Review. In the end it slipped in, supported by those, primarily the Prime Minister, who liked the sound of pluralism in financing without necessarily thinking through the consequences.

It is worth noting that the White Paper on community care (DoH, 1989c), responding to the Griffiths Report of 1988 *Agenda for Action*, which was addressed along with the NHS White Paper in the Health Service Bill of November 1989 which became the NHS and Community Care Act of 1990, also had as its essential element the distinction between the purchaser and the provider, with the assumption that rationing and choice are exercised by the purchaser (Griffiths, 1988).

THE POLITICS OF THE WHITE PAPER

Politically the White Paper can be seen as a clever exercise in diverting attention from the under-funding of the NHS by international standards (BMA 1988, 1989).

Under-funding occurs despite the fact that, also by international standards, the NHS is extremely efficient and effective at producing health outcomes from limited amounts of money. It is of course a contentious debate as to how much the health status of a country's population is related to its health service. There are those who point to the fact that differences in health status between social classes are as wide now as they were at the foundation of the NHS. The complexity of such debates apart, a good case can be made that the NHS has ameliorated what would have been an even worse situation. This is not to belittle the challenges still confronting public health in Britain; it is to point to the greater challenges which require greater expenditure.

The essence of the White Paper has been to focus attention upon the provision and management of health care. It is hoped that by decentralizing responsibility for provision to hospitals and units, the buck can be passed as regards adequacy and quality of service. Within hospitals, the buck can be passed to clinical directors within specialties, thereby sullying an interesting idea with unfortunate political connotations.

Devolution of management to the clinical specialty may have both advantages and disadvantages. Why not address these clinically? Consequences of under-funding can now be blamed more squarely on inefficient local managers who have allegedly been set free to manage. Health authorities are no longer to be representative institutions – the part-representative, part-appointed hybrid of the past – but slimmed-down executive management bodies. This development has some potentially positive features, especially given the uninformed political jerry-mandering of health care which can take place at the local level. Yet, in the context of the government's centralization of objectives but devolution of responsibility, the danger is that, as in other areas of public life, opposition to an over-reaching central government will be diminished.

The response of doctors was predictable. It was unfortunate for both the secretary of state and the doctors that the debate about the White Paper in general became confused with the debate about the new contract for GPs. Doctors' fears as to professional autonomy and levels of remuneration have been accompanied by a genuine fear that the benefits of a publicly planned NHS – which they have come to accept enthusiastically, however slowly – are in danger of being lost as a result of the White Paper. Much argument against the White Paper by clinicians and GPs has often been rooted in an altruistic defence of the Service, despite the fact that the BMA remains both an interest group and a trade union.

Hard-headed health service general managers, no longer the well-meaning but meddlesome lay administrators of the medical profession's rhetoric, are now much more agents of central policy than they have been in the past. Health authorities have become politicized in line with central government's wishes, as appointment of regional and district chairmen by the secretary of state has become much more dominated by party political considerations. General managers are now seen as spokesmen for the health service corporations which they direct; and in terms of loyalty, they are somewhat implausibly expected to combine the discretion of the civil servant with the evangelism of the private sector company director on behalf of ministerially defined health service objectives.

It is not surprising that the medical profession is on certain occasions both sceptical and obstructive when it comes to the implementation by managers of often ill-thought-out and politically motivated initiatives in the NHS, not least when these initiatives are given neither time nor resources to succeed before the next flavour of the month has taken over.

The NHS general manager is now partly a political appointment, expected to be 'one of us' in an increasingly politicized service, consistent with the government's politicization of public service. While there were significant and promising aspects of the White Paper, the politicized and ideological environment in which it was implemented held many dangers for a publicly planned health service, where resources were directed to those most in need. Ideologies and slogans were adopted from the language of competitive health care in the US which betrayed little knowledge of that country's mixed experience with competition. As in other areas of British public life, we have the irony that US-inspired competitive or privatization initiatives were uncritically fostered. When William Waldegrave became Secretary of State for Health in 1990, he had to ask for 'business language' to be toned down; this was confusing for those eager managers who had been having sleepless nights learning the new jargon.

The response of most other NHS professions, including nurses, paramedicals, and ancillaries, was hostile to the White Paper. The fundamental political reality was that any Secretary of State for Health would be reliant for career advancement upon making something of the implementation of the White Paper; and by the time further health policy was constructed, he or she might well be at another Ministry. There are those in the Conservative Party, inspired by the then Prime Minister Mrs Thatcher, who are distrustful of the idea of a publicly financed health service which is more than merely a welfare wedge for the poor. The prospect in 1991 was that such advisers could have their way in a fourth Conservative administration after the imminent general election.

It is the continual and recurring conflict between the pragmatists and such zealots which surfaced during the Prime Minister's Review. The right-wing think-tanks put forward radical ideas very much geared towards amending, if not replacing, the NHS, in the direction of both private financing and private provision. In the end, the public's strong belief in the NHS – and a number of severe difficulties in other policy areas – persuaded the Prime Minister that these think-tanks could not presently be risked with the comprehensive design of British health policy. The danger is that if the half-way house of partial competition which the White Paper embraces is seen to create severe problems for the NHS, it is open to the more radical wing of the Conservative Party to argue that full competition and greater privatization more generally are necessary to salvage things. A Labour government in the early 1990s does not mean the final death of such ideas, as long as a future Conservative victory remains likely.

THE POLITICS OF THE BMA

During the debate in 1989 about the White Paper, Secretary of State, Kenneth Clarke accused the BMA of always opposing radical change, whether that was the creation of the NHS and the debate leading up to that in the 1940s, or what Clarke sees as improvement to the NHS for the 1990s. The charge is highly misleading. There is no doubt that in the 1940s the BMA represented some hostility by doctors to the proposed NHS. In this they were largely supported by significant elements of the Conservative Party. So what has changed? Has the Conservative Party suddenly become the defender of the NHS? Has the BMA, in the guise of defending the NHS, simply continued its tradition of opposing meaningful and worthwhile reform?

The Conservative Party was always prepared to support private doctors in their fight to be free of government regulation, monitoring of contracts and monitoring of costs, as long as they were dealing with private patients not paid for substantially by the public purse. Once the NHS had been established and become both institutionalized and popular, Conservative governments, like Labour governments, found themselves paymasters of a publicly funded health care system. They were, therefore, interested in receiving value for money in this system. The medical profession, in turn, went from the position of opposition to the NHS, to one of support for its social ideals, with, of course, some exceptions, while showing some natural caution and reluctance to be over-monitored and over-regulated as to the cost and quality of services provided by doctors.

The irony is that, were we talking about the private sector, including private consumption of medical care, the Conservatives would in all likelihood be firmly supporting the doctors in their desire not to be over-regulated by schemes such as resource management, price controls and medical audit. The Conservative government wants to limit public spending on health care and regulate the medical profession accordingly, while encouraging private care which can set its own standards.

While Mr Clarke may not personally have designed or approved such a strategy, it was his fortune, or misfortune, to be the Minister of charge of presiding over exactly such a policy. There is a similar situation in the US, where government regulators on the right seek to cut costs and regulate to a great degree in the public sector, while leaving the private sector at least a bit more free from regulation. By and large, in the US, restrictions on prices in health care as represented by DRGs apply to

Medicare, but not directly to the private sector. Regulation is geared to saving public money, not linked to a universal strategy for equitably provided health care. The danger is that the same is now happening in the UK, albeit in a very different context. In Britain, the private sector is an escape from regulated, managed, or directed care, both for doctors and consumers. In the USA, the private sector is more regulated than in Britain.

Has the BMA been historically inconsistent? It has gradually changed its attitude, as has the medical profession as a whole. This is not to deny that there are some self-interested and over-cautious reactions to both the White Paper and other health care initiatives. The BMA has its conservative side. Doctors will always over-oppose regulatory schemes which affect them, as well as all professions. However, in portraying the BMA as opposing everything, Mr Clarke made selective use of the reality that the BMA's original opposition was to the NHS, and its opposition is currently geared to protecting the NHS.

The Conservative Party has undergone a more significant sea change. It is now leading the fight to regulate the medical profession, allegedly on behalf of the public interest, but in fact acting upon a desire to divert the terms of debate about the NHS away from funding levels by comparison with the rest of Europe.

THE DANGERS OF THE WHITE PAPER

The advantage of the NHS, by international standards, has been its cost-effective public provision through planning. This is in danger of being substantially lost. Even where intervention occurs, it will be through cumbersome regulation rather than systematic planning.

For example, self-governing hospitals are not allowed to 'cross-subsidise . . . to allow keener pricing of those services subject to competition' (Working Paper 1, p. 11). This would presumably require detailed public interest regulation. Protecting local services also requires cumbersome regulation, giving the lie to the idea that markets are more efficient and less bureaucratic. GP budgets, if subject to unforeseen pressure, are to be bailed out by district health authority contingency funds, as discussed in Working Paper 3 (Department of Health, 1989b). These require specially demarcated budgets, reducing flexibility. Furthermore, giving some GPs budgets for some hospital care will diminish the money available for districts' contracts with hospitals, increasing financial shortfalls for hospitals, which can only be made up by their selling services to GP practices. In practice, this will reduce the capacity for planning services based on awareness of long-term, stable, demand.

Overall, the creation of a number of distinct, cash-limited budgets leads to cost shifting – in other words, to attempts at reducing expenditure by shifting costs on to another budget. If districts or GPs have contracts, for example, for limited numbers of out-patient consultations, there will be a temptation to shift some referrals to Accident and Emergency. This is allegedly to be monitored, as stated in Working Paper 3, but the task is highly complex. GP referrals which later lead to intra- or inter-hospital, or tertiary, referral may have to be paid for out of GP budgets without the GP having knowledge in advance of the likely cost. Working Paper 3 expects the GP to foresee all. Regulatory labyrinths will increasingly be necessary to police the market; evolution of policy in 1991 bears this out.

The clause about self-governing hospitals and community units is the most damaging and irrelevant within the White Paper. Competitive principles, provider markets, and, in particular, the operation of the internal market, could have gone ahead without institutions opting-out. Suspicion of future full privatization was fuelled. Flexibility often means worse conditions for workers, unless those in scarce supply.

There was no statement as to outcomes or improvements expected from the new policy; the government fell into the trap of judging success by achievement of mechanistic management targets rather than health service (health status) outcomes. The policy, moreover, was always likely to be subverted. In the arena of education policy, schools sometimes sought to opt-out in order to subvert rational planning and avoid closure. Admittedly, while vigilance by the Department of Health could have stopped this happening in the health arena, a lot of managerial effort went into negotiations to seek to obtain local and short-term financial advantage from the policy. The political agenda overtook any rational management of the policy.

In the long term, if hospitals which opt-out of district health authority control and become self-governing succeed in selling their services to private purchasers, whether individuals, firms on behalf of their employees, or insurance groups acting as HMOs, then they will seek less and less of their core business from district health authorities or NHS GP practices. Unless a system of tight and intricate regulation which would make a nonsense of pro-competitive strategy, is brought into operation, or much more money is procured for the NHS, public services will have to be purchased substantially from a diminishing supply of directly managed NHS hospitals and units.

Medical, and perhaps other, staff at self-governing hospitals may be attracted by higher income and better conditions, forcing up prices and forcing the NHS's purchasing districts to shop elsewhere wherever possible – or to have less budget left for other, directly managed, units. This is already happening in London, where even trusts have been in financial difficulty.

There is little evidence from the US that, even when there are pressures to reduce costs, hospitals acting competitively are able to do so. This has applied even in recent years, when there has been an alleged glut of doctors in the US. There is anything but a glut in Britain: in fact, a main problem envisaged for the growth of the private sector is where the medical manpower and nursing manpower will come from. It can only come about through diminished supply of such manpower to the NHS, unless private medical education both takes off and expands quickly. That is why private hospitals or profitable NHS self-governing hospitals may bid up the salaries of doctors and the price of care, disadvantaging residual NHS institutions.

Given this scenario, there is likely to be a flight of provision from poor areas, with residual populations suffering as their institutions or GP practices become more rundown, with less subscriptions and less financing. The question is, competition to benefit who?

The danger of growing inegalitarianism will be increased if private money is encouraged into the system, whether through the purchasing of private health care in the hospital sector or through the admission, by any future legislation, of private money into the arena of primary care: for example, by allowing patients to top-up their publicly provided capitation payments with private resources. The verbal stress in the White Paper on capitation rather than on the tacitly retained, population-based, systematic system of RAWP (NHS management board, 1988) may be considered to be a prelude to greater stress upon the individual's needs, with the individual's right to pay being adopted in the future. Currently, this policy is advocated by right wingers, as they have also done in the education debate, in advocating that vouchers for schooling both be provided to parents and topped-up with private money where parents wish.

It is ironic to return the hospital sector – the whole system – to the unco-ordinated state of pre-1948. There was a good whiff of nostalgia in the reforms, despite their imagery of markets enhanced by high-tech corporate management. Government advisers openly interpreted their mission as to restore pre-1974 autonomy to hospitals such as Guy's. It is a shame also to restore pre-1948 raggedness and absence of planning, or rather, in the 1990s absence of coherent as opposed to panic planning. To dub opponents of the White Paper as nostalgic dreamers for 1948 is a travesty of the truth; fragmented provision and confused purchasing is hardly modern planning.

CONCLUSION

Apart from the rhetoric about markets, defenders of the White Paper talk of the need to ensure that money follows the patient; that workload is accompanied by reward. This is both reasonable and correct. Sometimes, bureaucratic means of trying to achieve this – the issue has not been ignored in the past – have been too slow, or have had unintended side-effects.

It is perfectly possible to relate reward to workload through flexible planning, without the disruption of the White Paper. Chapter 4 discusses practical issues concerning competition and planning.

Chapter Four

The White Paper: competition and planning in practice

COMPETITION *v.* PLANNING:
FROM A PLANNED NHS TO A MARKET PLACE?

An early reaction to the White Paper was to exclaim, 'Planning is dead!', to which one is tempted to add, 'Long live planning!' when faced with the need to plan a route out of competitive chaos.

It seemed that the era of a planned service was coming to an end. This was, of course, a paradox. The move to general management and the creation of an effective head office for the NHS, through first the management board and then the management executive after the White Paper, had as one of its overt premises the need to move away from a situation in which each of England's 14 regions was a mini-NHS, inadequately beholden to central policy directives. There was a forceful thrust of centralism behind the changes developing throughout the 1980s, only partially balanced in the rhetoric by devolution of responsibility for implementing them. Thus, to imply that a planned service was being replaced with a competitively based, market-oriented service, seemed on the surface very strange indeed.

It was never intended, once the more radical ideas presented to the Prime Minister's Review had been discarded, that the White Paper would mean an end to planning in the sense of gauging the need of populations and allocating resources accordingly. It is certainly true that the final formula for resource allocation to replace the former version of RAWP has many inadequacies and *non sequiturs*. Nevertheless, it remains a formula which attempts to gauge the need for health care and allocate money to regions, and by implication to districts, accordingly. This is of course resource allocation, not planning itself. Providing the resources is not the same as meeting the need on the ground.

To some extent, the decline of planning merely mirrors the rhetoric employed by the world of private business. Whereas the early 1970s were the heyday of corporate plans, planning gradually became a dirty word as management gurus advocated decentralization. The new slogan became corporate management, not corporate planning. Corporate management implied flexibility as well as control; loose as well as tight regulation of a company's divisions. In the NHS, there was in the events leading up to and immediately succeeding the White Paper no decision, overt or otherwise, to abandon planning in a more basic sense than the rhetorical or faddish one. If one identifies the need for health care in populations and seeks to provide resources to meet that need, it is a logical corollary to have a strategy to situate services which will meet the need in practice, whether these services are hospitals, community units, health centres, or whatever.

What the adoption of the internal-market theory – generalized to provider markets, which embrace the concept of private provision as well – seemed to mean for the NHS was that it would not be up to the centre or regions to dictate to districts where and how they provided services. Instead of districts receiving money and putting it, as it were, directly into bricks and mortar to provide services as much as possible for their local populations, there was to be a separation between the provision of the money to the purchaser and the provision of services by the provider. The district, of course, still owned the providers – the hospitals, units, and so forth, which had not become self-governing. Even self-governing trusts are allegedly fully part of the NHS, although not beholden to districts. Thus, there had to be a separation between purchasing and provision in practice as well as in theory. This was, however, a very artificial exercise in many respects. Districts in practice were still receiving the money and providing the services themselves, only going through the rigmarole of contracting with their providing units, i.e. contracting with themselves in order to fulfil the letter of the White Paper.

It did mean more than this. The idea of provider markets is that con-sumers – in most cases the district health authority, in some cases a GP practice with its own budget for certain categories of hospital care – shop around to find the provider who can satisfy their needs as consumers. The district is of course a consumer on behalf of its resident population. The aim is therefore that the district gauge needs, translate these into specific demands, ensure that these are satisfied by contracting with pro-viders, and adjusting contracts for the future to adjust to changed cir-cumstances or earlier mistakes. Internal planning in order to fulfil the purchasing function is certainly not dead.

What is conceivably dead as a result of the logic of the White Paper is regional planning. Regions no longer take top-down decisions as to where services should be sited throughout the region and what the service mix ought to be, influencing priorities by its capital allocations as well as its revenue allocations to districts; instead, regions merely parcel out the money and wait for districts to shop around in their purchasing rôle, buying some services from themselves and others from other districts, as well as conceivably the private sector, or other forms of care.

In practice this has not really happened. It would be anarchical for districts to shop around in a truly free market. For a start, effective markets imply the ability of providers to enter and leave the market quickly. This is not satisfied, and is not likely to be satisfied in the NHS; on the grounds of waste it is not desirable. What is therefore meant is a more restrictive version of the market: a system of contracting is likely to emerge, in which districts know where 90% of their care is to be bought, and merely shop around for deals at the margin. The interesting thing is that this was happening prior to the White Paper; the only thing necessary to make this a more systematic approach was to abolish the cross-boundary flow element of RAWP, so that when people living in one district were cared for by providers in another district, the money was able to be transferred directly as a market transaction, rather than automatically adjusted for in the RAWP formula.

Unless there is enough excess capacity to allow providers to sell their spare capacity in the marketplace quickly and flexibly, districts have to know where they are going to purchase their care from well in advance; and contracts have to cover various unforeseen circumstances – medical emergencies; sudden epidemics, and so forth – into the bargain. To prevent the new policy becoming a catastrophe, both economically and politically, regions became the steering mechanism by which districts set contracts – the umbrella under which districts were sheltered. There was thus a rôle for regions to be more activist in advising on or mandating the planning of services than pre-White Paper, a situation which more than one region were not slow to spot.

To move from the pre-White Paper NHS to the post-White Paper NHS and Community Care Bill NHS may be seen as a development and refinement of the logic of a publicly financed health sector. However, viewed from an international perspective, it may be seen as a retrograde step. Other systems are desperately trying to minimize the unpredictability, fragmentation, and inefficiencies caused by a separation of the purchaser and provider. What is hailed as a great achievement in Britain may be nothing of the sort. Setting up a market creates market incentives. When these market incentives are not to the good of the eventual consumer of services, what the Americans call 'gaming' is happening. No longer, for example, may it be rational for providers to share information with each other. Thus, the co-ordination of services, for example, between hospital and community, may be seriously affected.

Imbalances of knowledge between the provider and the consumer are what profit maximization in a marketplace is all about. It is not difficult to predict the effect upon the rational provision of health services which this may have. Markets imply marketing, and marketing implies persuading people to purchase what they do not need. We can live without that in an NHS which is not funded adequately to provide much of what people do need. Admittedly, economists and others have pointed out that need is a contentious and controversial concept; however, by any common-sense definition of need, it is very clear what is meant by saying that the NHS has difficulty within its current budget in meeting the needs of a community.

Unifying former marketplaces through planned provision has, interestingly, occurred within private companies – large corporations which realize that rather than have separate divisions it is rational to promote integration.

Internationally, it is considered more logical to move to an integration of purchasing and provision in health care. Britain is copying other systems' deficiencies, at a time when they may be planning to move away from those deficiencies! A separation of purchaser and provider may well be an impediment to clear location of services and cost and price control. NHS districts need to know the future mix of their own and other district services in order to plan for the needs of their patients. Moving to what is a very bureaucratic version of the marketplace in order to satisfy the government's rhetoric, yet preserve a modicum of common sense in the NHS, is hardly the efficiency for which the Conservative governments of the 1980s and later wished to be known.

Where there are not many competing providers, as in the NHS where there is very little excess capacity, instituting market incentives is likely to lead to monopoly providers where certain types of care are scarce, which will lead to a rise in costs. In turn, larger consortia of purchasers becomes necessary, to offset provider power. When such purchasers agree with GP fundholders how to contract with local providers, we are left with planning, but behind a confusing smokescreen of competition.

Definitions of Competition and Planning

The essence of competition is that a number of providers compete to satisfy a consumer or a number of consumers. If there is only one consumer, he or she will have what economists call 'monopsonistic' power, the analogy for consumers of monopolistic power by providers. A single purchaser of health care was viewed by many within the Prime Minister's Review as necessary to ensure that costs were not put up by pluralism in purchasing. However, introducing GP practices as alternative purchasers, and boosting private care generally, is likely to provide a pluralism in finance which is not particularly efficient. Additionally, it can threaten the viability of providers which districts may wish to preserve or protect. Planning, on the other hand, consists in identifying need and mandating its provision without competition.

When one hears about planning in the private sector and planning in the NHS, one may want to go back to first principles and ask what is the difference between planning and competition? After all, if Sainsburys assess the need or demand in a particular area for their goods, and locate stores accordingly, that is surely planning.

Two points should be made: firstly, Sainsburys are likely to be doing this along with other competitors, and seeking to push them as far as possible out of the marketplace. So, to have true competition in the NHS would mean many more providers – at much greater cost – than is ever likely to happen. Secondly, need is a separate concept from demand. Demand is what consumers with resources register in the marketplace, hopefully to be satisfied by providers. Need in health care is obviously related to demand. If people have what they themselves perceive as needs, and have the resources, they will presumably demand the product, for example, access to health care, whether curative or preventive. However, individuals' definitions of needs may differ from experts' definitions of needs. Furthermore, needs may not be registered, because of lack of resources on the part of individuals, a major reason for the existence of the NHS in the first place. Finally, demands may be registered which do not reflect needs. Even the individual will be prepared to acknowledge that he or she does not really need something, but is willing to demand it anyway. Nevertheless, for our purposes we can see a strong correlation between demand and need.

A planning system seeks to provide services to meet need, taking a number of assumptions into account. In health care, these assumptions are likely to concern the size of populations; likely health demands from a population based on statistical as well as conceptual work; the willingness of people to travel various distances; the reasonableness of travelling different distances attributed to people by planners; the cost of different options and the likely benefits; value judgements as to which categories of care group should receive services given the necessary choice due to shortage of resources; and so forth.

All of these will eventually produce a mix of services, for example throughout a region. It makes sense, for economic purposes as well as for social equity, to ensure that the catchment areas covered by planning are as large as possible. In the NHS, the region is an appropriate level. For if the populations the planner is dealing with are too small, miscalculations are less likely to average out. More importantly, operating budgets will be too low to allow for flexibility, and lack of flexibility is more likely to lead to a denial of care to individuals.

Competition, on the other hand, implies purchasers handling manageable budgets, and procuring goods from competing providers. The advantages of large-scale planning are likely to be lost. There is no attempt to deny that planning can be top-heavy and bureaucratic. More promising in an NHS context would be examination of the options for increasing the flexibility of planning without throwing it all up in pursuit of an untried ideology in health care. It is untried in the sense that a competitive provider market has not so far been combined with a nationally publicly financed NHS. It has certainly not been untried in the more general sense of the market in health care, which has been tried and found seriously wanting.

It is often thought that competition is efficient because it uses the price mechanism as well as giving incentives to providers to compete with each other. However, there is no reason why a planning system cannot use costing systems, which are in effect the prices. In any case, we are not talking about private profit, and therefore a lot of the incentives of a marketplace may be diminished. The types of incentive which remain in public markets may be important, but they are not likely to have the force of private markets. The sort of incentive available, for example to the manager of the hospital, will be to reward staff if they maximize their workload and maximize the income of the hospital. This will depend upon what the Government is prepared to allow in terms of pay flexibility.

A perfectly legitimate defence of the White Paper is that by giving budgets to district health authorities which reflect only the needs of their resident populations and not the needs of the people they currently serve, the district is able to make 'rational' decisions as to the relative need for their residents, and purchase services accordingly. Admittedly, a regional planning model may site services perfectly according to the planner's criteria, but it will not be able to prevent residents from one district using services more than another, unless by fairly unpalatable regulation of access to hospitals. At least giving districts budgets ensures that the money is spent on the residents: if the money allocated to districts is done properly, or at least as well as can be achieved, then there is a better guarantee that the money at least will be spent on those for whom it is needed. That is the one main advantage of separating the purchaser and provider. For example, some of the regions in the NHS had adopted systems loosely known as 'regional strategic management' by academics, which model the needs of communities, model catchment populations, and provide services accordingly. However, usage is often not as intended by the planners, which causes difficulty with the planning process.

The question remains, can this alleged advantage of the White Paper be achieved without the destructive consequences of the White Paper? The answer is that it can. Models involving a simulated market involve the allocation of money to providers based on catchment populations, as a result of the modelling of services, without going through pseudo-competitive rigmarole to achieve their ends. They take the textbook advantages of competition – incidentally, unlikely to be realized in the real world – and seek to realize them through a planning system.

Finally, what about the widespread belief, which owes as much to events in Eastern Europe in 1989 and 1990 as the neo-conservative politics of many Western countries in the 1980s, that planning is bureaucratic, unwieldly, and inefficient and most definitely yesterday's panacea? Many variants of planning occur which are laudable, in so called capitalist countries as well as the formerly Communist countries, that is, the intelligent use of public resources to meet need in a democratic system monitored in the end by a democratic parliament.

One should not under-estimate the ingenuity of health authorities to get around dogmatic pro-competitive instructions from the government. If, for example, it is believed that instituting a market would lead to monopoly power being exerted by certain providers, for example, self-governing trusts, then districts will seek to merge to form consortia so that they will be powerful purchasers. If regional planning is being discouraged, then consortia districts may restore it by the back door. That is, the institutional and organizational shape of the health service in response to the White Paper is likely to be substantially different from what it is today.

As with Griffiths of 1983, only on a much larger scale, what is not supposed to be a reorganization has as usual turned out to be the biggest reorganization of them all so far. Soon after the White Paper and Working Papers were published, districts sought to co-opt the agenda to their own advantage by seeking to opt out as whole districts: self-governing trusts would consist of whole districts as providers. It was soon made known that the Department of Health would disallow this. The question would have arisen, who is the purchaser if the whole district is the provider? One answer would be the region. A more likely answer would be that the purchasing function can be wholly separated from the provision function, and both handled by the district. If so, the exercise would be a nonsense.

Less extreme examples of attempts to implement the letter but not the spirit of the White Paper were soon becoming institutionalized practice within a few years of the whole episode. Post-White-Paper events can of course be used by the government also to fulfil their objectives. For example, certain ambulance services were allowed to constitute themselves as self-governing trusts and sell their services. This is merely allowing flexible pay by another route.

Political factors will be the most significant of all in determining the future of the NHS following the White Paper. After all, the whole debate about providers becoming self-governing trusts was not determined by economic logic or clinical logic, but by the political need for units to be seen to be willing to be self-governing trusts in order to attract government money. Even the process of allocating capital is likely to favour self-governing trusts rather than directly managed units which remain fully within the managerial control of the NHS. While one should not overlook the economic logic informing the White Paper, one should equally not be surprised if it is suspended whenever convenient in order to allow a jerrymandered marketplace to be controlled by the government.

Following the replacement of Kenneth Clarke by William Waldegrave as Secretary of State for Health, and later of Margaret Thatcher by John Major as Prime Minister, the radical elements of competition were played down. This was primarily for reasons of electoral safety-first. But a substantive reason based on the logic of policy also has applied. Either competition leads to closures, expansions and radical changes in health care provision, or the rhetoric of competition is partially retained yet general managers are encouraged to make little change in practice as to where referrals of patients are made. In 1991, the latter was occurring. The longer term is unpredictable, but at present any government is saddled with a lot of upheaval and demoralization of professional staff, for very limited policy aims.

HEALTH SERVICE OBJECTIVES: THE MARKET AND PLANNING

The main objectives of the White Paper, apart from the right-wing political agenda, have been to promote the costing of services; the making of contracts by purchasers with providers to ensure that these services are delivered; and the resulting greater efficiency of the NHS. The Paper has also embraced the theory of competing providers, and pluralism in financing to some extent, although this was a controversial element opposed by many of the right wingers involved in the Prime Minister's Review.

The aim of accurately costed services which providers contract to provide to consumers can be produced without a marketplace. A planning system attempts to cost services, decide on the location of provision of services, decide on which institutions provide what, and then effectively leads to contract between the purchasing agent (the region or district) and the provider. Thus, in some ways the White Paper will merely be formalizing existing planning practice.

The irony is that a planning-led system may fulfil the same better than a competitive system. There may be problems in practice, such as those associated with any large-scale enterprises, public or private, but if the purchasing body has direct responsibility for the providing body – if the basic thrust of the White Paper, the separation of the provider and the consumer, is not relevant – then the health authority has direct control over its providers. The advantage claimed by supporters of the White Paper for a separation of the provider and the consumer – that it separates the responsibility for provision from responsibility for the regulation of provision – is an important point because monitoring of services should take place by a party independent of the provider. The White Paper advocates the purchaser will be able to do this; however, it is perfectly possible for an independent commission to guarantee service, and quality to be instituted. Indeed, independent quality assessment is better.

If provision of services is at stipulated prices in accordance with NHS priorities, as expressed by local purchasers of services (mostly districts), then gaming by providers is a real possibility. The only way to avoid loss-leading in some specialties where there is a need to be competitive in providing, and cross-subsidies from other specialties where the provider can get away with higher prices, is to have a system of standard pricing.

This has many unsatisfctory features. Firstly, it puts pressure on providing authorities to compete in order to make their internal profit by lowering costs alone rather than by offering a higher-quality product at a higher price – for example, for those purchasers of services (districts and GPs) who wish that. In the former Soviet Union, experiments in health care markets led to polyclinics purchasing services from hospitals at guaranteed prices. Secondly, the basis of a fixed-price contract would have to be established. Would it be, for example, through the use of DRGs, which are an attempt at costing, not pricing? Is any profit margin to be allowed?

Such analysis is intended to illustrate that if the NHS, whether nationally or locally, is to decide upon its health priorities and plan for the provision of services accordingly, it may be better to do so directly rather than through a market mechanism. A market mechanism may distort the relative costs, rather than prices, of alternative services and make the realization of the purchasers' priorities more difficult, not easier. The marketplace will not work as idealists wish: if a health provider has a virtual monopoly of one type of service, the price may be unreasonably high, and a district's purchasing priorities may be distorted if it is to buy that service; its service mix will not be as desired. The only alternative is a bureaucratic form of regulation which will make competition like planning.

It is important to prevent exploitation by providers of imperfect markets, and to ensure the appropriate mix of cost and quality as well as overall service mix – the overall planning remit pre- and post-White Paper of a district health authority as well as the regional health authority. Opted-out hospitals merely compound this difficulty, as they have their own financial incentives separate from service-providing needs of the purchasing district or GP. Using the market at the edges of a planning policy will, however, have the advantage of allowing flexibility within an overall planning structure. Relying on a White-Paper-style market, with contracts as a means of enforcing an internal market, whether with or without opted-out hospitals, will be a much more inflexible system than one in which the financier and provider are the same.

There is allegedly no dispute about the main service objective of the NHS, which might be described as providing a service mix determined in a compromise between national and local priorities, difficult as that is in practice, at acceptable cost for providers, acceptable in terms of distance and quality *inter alia* to providers. Regional and district budgets ought to be monitored at the detailed level in order to ensure that priorities are not only established but met in the provision of services at the micro level. There is no evidence that the White Paper's system of allocation of resources will achieve this better than a system of planning.

The market and incentives

The government in 1989 assumed that the financial discipline of the market would encourage hospitals to seek profit, and would encourage, for example, GPs to use their budgets judiciously. If this was indeed the over-riding incentive, the government seemed to assume that it would be quietly laid to one side in order to protect the consumer. For example, it was not anticipated that GPs would attempt to keep more expensive patients off their lists; it was not anticipated that hospitals would suspend their social obligations with their community in providing core services, even if government regulation was inadequate to protect these services to the last detail.

It is, of course, fair to argue that under the pre-White Paper system of allocating resources to regions, districts, and then hospitals, there was no guarantee that money would be spent according to social priorities. If there is no adequate costing of activity, then resources may not be spent on the activities which the government, the regional health authority, the district health authority, or even the doctor operating the budget wishes to see pursued. Choices as to social priorities, let alone to economic cost-effectiveness, will not be possible. The aims of the White Paper – to reward workload and to allow choices to be made given the knowledge of costs – are laudable aims. However, it is important to pursue them in a manner which does not give incentives to key decision-makers (the board of management of opted-out hospitals; district managers; doctors) to disobey community or government priorities in health care. The White Paper has almost nothing to say about priorities in health care.

The Labour Party's document, *A Fresh Start* (1990) suggested that Labour would retain the managerial aspects of the White Paper which allow better costing and determination of priorities. The Labour Party does not accept less democratic health authorities, constituted on private company board lines. The rhetoric of the market and competition, such as it remained in 1991, is replaced in Labour policy by service agreements between health authorities (purchasers) and their providers. Opting-out is reversed, and so the purchaser–provider split is diminished in import as well as in rhetoric.

Labour seeks to plan for priorities, using more flexible planning norms than in the past – for example, rewarding districts which achieve better health status for their populations. This still leaves open the question as to how the inefficient or ineffective districts' populations could best be protected. As a result, Labour's policy documents of February 1992, outlined a system of performance agreements to tackle such problems.

Convergence between competition and planning?

A convergence between the aims of planning and the aims of the market may be illustrated by a particular debate which arose around the 1989 White Paper. Making districts responsible for the purchase, but not necessarily for the provision, of services for their populations has been associated with the opting-out of hospitals and the granting of budgets for hospital care to GPs who qualify and who want them. The aim is to promote rival purchasing agents, but, more importantly, rival providing institutions so that efficient allocations and decisions can be made.

A major problem with allowing hospitals to opt-out and then contract for the provision of services to health districts is that they may hold a monopoly position. If, for example, a district loses in terms of the resource-allocation formula, such as the West Lambeth District in London, containing both St Thomas's and Guy's Hospitals, and it is felt that these hospitals are worthy providers of care, then an internal market model may allow other districts to receive the needed redistribution of money for their populations, yet use, for example, Guy's and St. Thomas's when purchasing services. The internal market thus may prevent unnecessary duplication of services.

If, however, an opted-out hospital such as Guy's is not to abuse its market position, it may have to have its price regulated, just as many markets in other policy areas have to be regulated to allow the textbook of advantages of competition to be achieved more satisfactorily. The means of imputing a reasonable price to such hospitals for different specialties or specific diagnoses may be through a British adaptation of the DRG system. Thus a competitive model may use exactly the same tool as its alleged opposite, a regional strategic planning model. DRGs, were advocated as a means by which regions ought to impute costs to services when modelling, planning, and, resultingly, allocating resources in a planning-led model.

The main difference is that when an activist region plans services and funds institutions accordingly, in proportion to workload, there is no doubt about whether the service is provided. In a market model, this doubt may lead to duplication of services as different hospitals compete in the short-term.

This is not necessarily fatal criticism, for the planning model also has disadvantages: it may be cumbersome, too centralist, and too much a remote scientific exercise which does not take into account political realities at the district and unit level. Uncertainty about the location or provision of services which is too radical may be damaging. For example, the major aim of the internal-market policy as advocated specifically by Enthoven may have been to save the bacon of hospitals such as Guy's without abandoning the redistributive goals of the resource allocation formula (RAWP) and its associated movement of money out of London. The aim is still to redistribute the money, yet not damage the facilities in the districts which are losing the money.

In a market-trading model, the unpredictability of capital cost – which must be accounted for in order to set a realistic price, in that the institution has been charged for capital either in the private market or by the district if it is an NHS-incorporated hospital – means that it is unknown whether such hospitals will be able to compete effectively in the market or not. They may be the providers of the best quality of medical care in certain specialties, they may be the most obvious providers, and services may not exist at the same level in other districts.

A market decision nevertheless involves an estimate as to cost effectiveness; and for reasons which have little to do with the efficiency of the hospital, such as its location in an expensive part of London, its prices may lead to other districts concluding that they would rather develop their own services than to send patients there. Thus, the internal market may in fact provide a boost to district self-sufficiency, its very opposite.

That is why the stated goals of the 1989 White Paper may be very similar to the stated goals of regional planning, yet the consequences of the different routes in practice may be very different. It is only by reference to theory and faith that one can point to the advantages and disadvantages of the market model.

Anomalies and outrages

The media soon spotted one anomalous consequence of marketing in the NHS. In one rôle, districts are purchasers for their residents, and in another, the head office of providers, seeking to maximize profit from other districts and purchasers generally. Directly managed units, which are not self-governing, are of course seeking to raise revenue for their parent districts, if the market is operating.

Thus district A can sell services to district B, involving B's patients coming to A. Meanwhile, it may be denying local care to its own residents, as the purchasing budget of A is exhausted, or a better deal is available in district C. So B is sending its patients to A, which in turn is sending its patients to C, in a particular specialty.

This has actually been happening in a triangle involving Coventry, Shropshire, and Wales. Can it be rational? If B wants to buy its residents services in A why is A not buying its residents in A, i.e. locally? Because, it could be answered, it is better – more cost-effective; particular clinical needs – to send them to C. It could be that C is best/cheapest, but that transport costs and travel practicalities rule out B's patients going to C. A is second-best.

But this is an unlikely, if possible, explanation. It is more likely that the vagaries of the contracting system are creating an anomalous situation, outrageous to patients not interested in market textbooks, but interested in why they are being sent to distant care which is expensive and which prevents relatives visiting.

To cost different choices and options as to location of care properly, transport costs should be included in an appraisal of the costs of sending patients to non-local services. But economic logic is only partially drawn on by the government and an increasing number of those health authorities beholden to it, as the politicization of health authority appointments and reappointments, even prior to the White Paper, was continuing apace.

Consultants in district A's real-world equivalents do not understand why they cannot be financed to treat their own patients. Patients wonder why everyone is playing musical chairs (or musical British Rail Cheap Returns) to get care. If there is an economist's explanation, it has to be a good one.

From service planning to internal business planning

Service planning in the NHS has meant that in ideal circumstances the services required by client groups and populations have been provided in appropriate locations. Additionally, the required mix of services, ranging from in-patient to out-patient, to community to primary, has been the responsibility of health authorities.

Contracting with competing providers means that purchasing authorities still have the obligation to contract for services to fulfil such service mixes. The difficulty is in seeking to ensure that contracts with acute providers, for example, tie in with contracts for after-care services in the community. Instead of an integrated approach to service delivery by direct management of complementary services, we will now have atomized contracts with no incentives for providers to co-operate with the patient's total package of care in mind. There may be incentives for each service of each department to maximize workload, but that is a separate matter.

Ironically, when many other countries are seeking to remove sources of fragmentation in care delivery, Britain is seeking through legislation to institutionalize a lack of co-operation between complementary service providers in the name of provider markets, whether competitive or not.

Service planning has to accommodate flexibility, and the need for plans to change over time as needs change or as predictions are amended. But multi-scenario planning is possible where necessary as a more flexible variant of traditional planning; throwing out the baby of planning with the bathwater of inflexibility is not necessary.

Planning is now to mean business planning, or internal planning by providers, to meet needs identified in purchasers' global business plan. Regulation may ensure that the best of the NHS's comprehensiveness is preserved. But the question is begged, why such a ticklishly difficult diversion in the name of an ideology waning from its temporary revival before its effects in health care are registered?

RELATIVE ADVANTAGES AND DISADVANTAGES OF COMPETITION AND PLANNING WITHIN REGIONS

Competition: market trading by districts

For

- Redistribution of resources (formerly sub-regional RAWP) can be accomplished more quickly, to a clearly defined level (district), allowing districts to be purchasers of care.
- Certain incentives can be developed, in theory, to encourage overt decisions as to specialization, economies of scale, and trade-offs as to which services to buy where.
- Losing districts can recoup money by selling services.

Against

- May achieve its opposite, i.e. district self-sufficiency! Districts will perhaps not trade for political, social, professional and interest-group reasons.
- May subvert useful *ad hoc* rationing by doctors, and replace it with institutionalized rationing by purchasers.
- May subvert the positive side of localism in the NHS: links between a district's hospital and community services, on the one hand, and GP services, on the other.

Planning: regional strategic management (planning of services on a region-wide basis)

For

- Allows stability and predictability in service development.
- May be a better replacement of the cumbersome, pre-White-Paper system of allocating resources to districts than post-White-Paper markets, because disincentives to increasing one's workload are abolished without the confusion of new pricing systems being used for direct charging. Resources can be planned to follow the patient/ workload without leaving it to the unpredictable market. Markets can only work well if there are adequate resources to allow excess capacity and the luxury of failed investment. In any case, markets do not work quickly enough in health care, e.g. in constructing or removing hospitals to reflect demands.

Against

- Does not guarantee that hitherto relatively under-funded districts will actually be the ones whose populations will benefit from new orientation and location of services even if the strategic modelling is geared to this.
- May have the disadvantages of 'dirigiste' planning.
- It takes power over allocations away from districts.

Evaluation

Regional strategic management is capable of effective, flexible planning, if properly used. The question is, is it compatible with the new NHS culture – accountability yet devolution? Given the de facto centralization of the post-White-Paper NHS, including the fixing of the market, this reason for opposing regional planning may be disingenuous. In practice, however, there is now consensus around the principle of district planning for need. Whereas the Conservatives seek competition in provision, Labour encourages local provision within community-based health authorities.

THE ESSENTIAL CONTRAST BETWEEN THE PRE-WHITE-PAPER NHS AND THE POST-WHITE-PAPER NHS

Rationing within the NHS before the White Paper, was informal and tacit. GPs had the right of freedom of referral without overt consultation with health managers or others. Money did not always follow the patient, and rationing was achieved by virtue of waiting-lists both for in-patient and out-patient services in different parts of the country, as well as by general availability or otherwise of services, and general assessment and behaviour of GPs. In other words, rationing was conducted at the point of provision.

The essence of the White Paper was that the purchasing of health care ought to be rationed 'rationally', with district managers as the central rationers. They are now responsible for placing contracts for the delivery of both core and other services with providers in their own district, with providers outside their district, and in the private sector. In addition, GPs fulfilling certain criteria are allowed to hold their own budgets for certain categories of hospital care. It has been anticipated by some that in the longer run the rôle of private financing and private insurance in health care will increase to provide more pluralism on the demand side.

The alleged aim is to stimulate competitive advantages by instituting a system of competing providers, who effectively tender for provision of both core and other services. Thus, rationing decisions are taken at the point of consumption. GPs' referrals have to be in line with overall budgetary criteria for the use of hospital and community care. Money may now follow the patient, but it is no longer the GP or the GP in consultation with the patient who decides where the patient and money are sent. Referrals involve complex negotiations between purchasers (districts), GPs, and providers. In none of this is the patient directly represented. Instead, purchasers seek good deals, GPs seek to protest their referral preferences, and providers obey the incentives, good and bad, of the market.

The essence of this competitive strategy is also followed in the Griffiths II proposals for co-ordinating the financing for community care. The theory again is that a global purchaser can identify needs on behalf of the population requiring services, and contract with competing providers to provide these services.

The NHS/Community Care Bill of 1989/90 had as its essence the separation of purchasing and provision in health care.

Another major constituent of the White Paper concerns its strategy for devolving responsibility for handling management problems away from the centre. While politicians and others at the centre still define the health-policy agenda (and indeed, the health management agenda) accountability upwards, devolution of implementation it is hoped will take the heat off Ministers. This is part of an overall political strategy to divert attention from the debate about funding of the NHS and priorities within the NHS to a debate about the institutional mechanics of health service provision. The overwhelming early priority of the new NHS management executive has been to deal with the thorny and often irrelevant question of hospitals opting-out.

Unfortunately, and despite prevailing rhetoric, the health policy debate and measurement of the success of health policy and management continues to be conducted in terms of inputs and outputs rather than outcomes. Some of the key health challenges – to do with equitable access across social classes to better health status and services, and some key public health challenges associated with this task – are still being left on one side. *The Health of the Nation* (DoH, 1991) falls far short of this task.

In practice, the chief executive of the NHS management executive may run the risk of being a Ministerial side-kick, bearing responsibility without power. Speaking for the government under the guise of neutral independent management on, for example, an ambulance dispute will always be more pressing than devising health management priorities independently of the government's current political priorities.

The introduction of general management into the NHS after 1983 was intended to strengthen central control, not weaken it, while devolving operational responsibility. The first Griffiths Report arose from initial government determination to fix NHS labour after the 1982 industrial dispute; from the subsequent insistence by Griffiths that his inquiry be widened from manpower to management generally, and the concurrent view of the government that Department of Health lay administration be replaced by professional management at the apex of the NHS, to copy other public corporations.

The 1989 White Paper took central political control further and made NHS managers more than ever part corporate loyalists, part civil servant bureaucrats, rather than locally based part independent administrators. As with Griffiths in 1983–4, it was never intended that decentralization of power should occur within the NHS; it could be argued that responsibility to Parliament prevents this. The White Paper furthermore accepts the pragmatism of public responsibility and political management in a way that the Griffiths Report did not, in that it provides for a political policy board to which the management executive is directly responsible. In the Griffiths Inquiry Report, the management board is the apex and the supervisory board was a more amorphous entity – later to fall into disuse as Ministers gradually took over the management board. After the first management board Chairman, Mr Victor Paige, resigned in June 1986, there had in fact been minimal distinction between Ministerial control via the supervisory board and a Ministerially-dominated management board. Mr Tony Newton, Minister of State for Health, was Chairman of both.

The NHS of the future may derive benefit from tight central control and yet devolved operational responsibility. But it will only do so if political interference does not set management's agenda, and if strategic management stresses health outcomes rather than short-term processes. There are those who will think this a tall order.

Rationing rationally at the point of consumption of health care rather than *ad hoc* at the point of supply is the intention, but political fixing will be the result. The overall dilemma facing an exponent of competition in health care is whether the intended benefits of competition, even where the marketplace works, outweigh the major costs which such a policy will impose in practice. Even a successful market requires duplication by competitive suppliers, and failures as well as successes.

If the hospital or district knows that the level of funding it receives is dependent upon its ability to sell itself, long-term planning for need will not be possible. Investment decisions may be rational if a particular caseload, perhaps involving economies of scale, is assumed, but irrational if a different scenario in fact applies. Any marketplace faces these uncertainties; however, a publicly financed health sector, subject to more rather than less political control as the years of supposed individualism progress, is hardly the best location for instituting free-market principles. It is unlikely that pure free-market principles will be allowed to operate if the politicians' agenda dictates otherwise.

The complex nature of health care, and the fact that many conditions necessary for the operation of the free market are not met in health care mean that the role of the market is in any case limited. Competing to provide complex services requiring long-term investment, long-term manpower planning, whether central or indicative, and complex inter-specialty links and dependencies may be a cumbersome rather than an efficient way of meeting need.

It is with this type of factor in mind that health authorities have sought, in some instances, to co-opt the agenda contained in the White Paper: for example, by proposing that whole districts, rather than simply hospitals or units, opt-out and become self-governing entities. The essence of becoming self-governing is that there is financial freedom and independence, by comparison with institutions which do not opt-out. Allowing a whole district to opt-out would, claim such districts, allow the district to retain the function of global planning, while receiving their funds with less interference from the centre.

If districts were to opt-out in full, it would force regions to become the contracting agency rather than the districts, unless districts were to contract with themselves. We would indeed have a policy of regional planning of services, albeit embraced under the rhetoric of competition.

Chapter 5 reviews the key elements of contracting from a strategic rather than from an operational viewpoint; implications for the relationship of provider with purchaser; the implications for new services; and the political agenda infusing such complex issues. For the language spoken by NHS managers, post-1990, is often very different from the language understood by their political masters.

Chapter Five

Implementing the White Paper: the evolving agenda

CONTRACTS AND CONTRACTING: COMPETITION OR CHAOS?

The purpose of contracting is primarily to instil efficiency into the provision of services. The NHS Review represented an attempt to argue that the NHS did not need more money but that existing resources could be used, or stretched, to do more. Like competitive tendering for domestic services, general tendering for all clinical services, to win contracts, was thought to involve greater efficiency along the lines of theory propounded by pro-competitive economists.

Unfortunately, the negative effects of competitive tendering may ensue. Wages and conditions of providing staff may be forced or held down. Quality of care may suffer as patients are discharged early to keep providers' costs low. Without high-quality community services and community care, such patients may fall between two stools. After all, the NHS and the Community Care Act create similar downward-cost pressures for community care.

What Americans call 'gaming' may follow as providing hospitals and units seek to make enough profit on those activities which they can supply as a monopoly in order to sell competitive services at unrealistically low prices. The Department of Health has prohibited such cross-subsidies, but if information is not available to allow accurate pricing, it is not available to monitor this, or indeed to allow providers to know whether they are doing so or not!

Even where such tricks are not forthcoming, a more serious situation may arise. Providers now have to market themselves to purchasers, rather than to provide according to regional and district provision plans. As a result, lots of effort will go into business planning, production planning, marketing and contracting. Not only will this diminish the NHS's record of low administrative costs (an irony, given the alleged desire of the Review to stretch existing resources), but it will encourage providers to keep information about services to themselves; to seek to maximize income rather than only meet need; to distort prices through cross-subsidy despite cumbersome regulation to try to limit it; and therefore to prevent all needs from being met.

There will be the danger of a bias towards large monopoly providers, with higher costs than now in the long term squeezing out 'Cinderella' activities. Only by destroying national pay bargaining, through the pay review bodies and Whitley Councils, can already poorly paid workers in Cinderella services be encouraged to preserve their services and jobs by taking pay cuts. The exceptional cases where pay rises follow from market policies, for example in NHS trusts for scarce categories of staff, will of course be heavily publicized.

If purchasers insist on a balanced-care mix at reasonable prices, then providers' business plans will in the end be nothing more than contributions to current NHS planning under a new name. Contracts, after all, are not to be legally enforceable. Tenders by providers, the successful ones of which form the basis for contracts, will contain much detail; but inspection of the Department's document, *Contracting* (February 1990) containing model contracts, shows that the detail is either to the level of generality, or else contains impractically mechanistic clauses, for example, covering quality. It is no surprise that such contracts are not to be legally enforceable: quality is likely to play second fiddle to the need for low costs and high quantity provision.

Block contracts will dominate. These are nothing more than reimbursed services, as at present, without recourse to volume figures. Hence, providers may not have any more ability to be reimbursed according to workload than at present. Cost-per-volume contracts will be helpful in this regard at least. Cost-per-case contracts will be rare.

The need to preserve reserves to pay for care for which contracts have not been placed will mean that resources disposed of through contracts will be less than the total quantum of current resources. This will mean either cuts, or contracts involving deficit spending, by purchasers. Such reserves are to cover GP referrals not in line with purchaser contracts – a major hurdle to overcome – and emergency in-patient care (out-patients are to be absorbed in providers' block contracts).

Unless GPs' rights are to be severely restricted, contracts will not be a radical change. In practice, contracts will reflect existing service patterns, and will merely be a bureaucratic means of doing what is already done. The rhetoric pervading health services management is understandable given government pressure, but needs to be tempered by a healthy dose of scepticism.

Contracts should be a chance for purchasers to define new needs or unit needs, make priorities, and contract to have them provided. Separating purchaser and provider can help to prevent provider capture. But in practice, purchasers and providers will be too close to allow beneficial effects of this to be clearly obtained in most cases.

Managed competition?

In the US, the idea of managed competition has been promoted as a means of combining market incentives to both providers and consumers with at least minimal social objectives. In other words, however unpopular the word is, there should be regulation of provider behaviour, as well as guarantees of purchasing power by the poor, in the more ambitious versions of the idea, such as that prepared by Enthoven.

The increasing perception throughout 1990 that free competition in health care was largely impossible, and both inefficient and unfair to the extent it was possible, led to adoption of the slogan 'managed competition' in Britain also.

The irony is that in Britain there was no need to create a troublesome market and then seek to regulate it. The two greatest arguments for a marketplace in health care involving contracts with providers were allegedly to reward providers in proportion to their workload, and to ensure that contracts reflected the health care needs of district populations as defined by purchasers (district authorities).

But neither of these requires a market. Increasing the bite of effective general management, to ensure that providers offer a mix of services representing need, and to ensure that resource allocation reflects workload, would offer a means of achieving these ends through public control rather than regulation of private incentive, so often problematic and open to subversion in practice.

By April 1990, the Secretary of State for Health was denying that competitive markets were at the heart of the White Paper. Interviewed on BBC 1's 'Panorama' on 30 April, he attributed the view that the White Paper was all about competition to the propaganda of his opponents. The question must then be asked, why did the government allow damaging ideas to be promoted if only to deny them later?

The answer lies in the politics of the NHS Review. Right-wingers held sway at various stages, including the then Prime Minister. It was only by early 1990, with the Prime Minister's attention on electoral survival, and the poll tax in particular, rather than the detail of other domestic policy, that Kenneth Clarke and the Department of Health could seek to translate the impact of the White Paper into at least partly pragmatic health policy without interference from the ideological right. Sir Roy Griffiths now deputy chairman of the NHS policy board, was one of the many pragmatists who sought to deny that competition and separating the purchaser from the provider were the holy grail. Sir Roy was more concerned to develop general management further in the pursuit of greater efficiency and effectiveness.

If competitive forces were to thrive, there is circumstantial evidence that it could be disastrous for equity and availability of services. The need for purchasers to put aside money for emergencies, and negotiate low prices would lead both to less money for normal services and to limits on the quality of care. A pursuit of quantity could easily threaten quality. Simulated management games modelling the operation of the market in one NHS region (East Anglia), suggested this (The *Guardian*, 17 May 1990).

Providers in turn would discharge patients early to cut costs unless heavy regulation prevented it. Such regulation would be more cumbersome than public planning, and if it were unsuccessful, the strain on community services would be great.

Contracts could incorporate both a concern for quality and effective resource management, but only if, firstly, more money was available; secondly, providers had stable sources of finance; and, thirdly, purchasers were able to translate the measurement of populations' needs into effective contracts.

Instead, much energy went into developing new purchasing consortia (mega-districts) and provider monopolies. Staff, from top management to ground level, were frequently demoralized by yet another mammoth reorganization, again in all but name. Some regions took the reorganization as yet another chance to slim district as well as regional staff, since now districts as purchasers were to be skeleton organizations by comparison with the previous districts as providers.

In practice, of course, the separation was often chimerical. All it meant was less streamlined planning and more bureaucracy. Fragmented and uncertain provision, only overcome by cumbersome regulation, was ironically what NHS supporters had previously detected in other systems.

Resource allocation to the NHS, and to regions and districts, was still of course on a scientific basis, from the public purse. The Service's basic financing structure had not changed, yet the preconditions for privatization of provision, were any future government so to wish, had been established.

Providers were, for example, to pay capital charges, and their prices to purchasers were to reflect total costs (capital plus recurrent). This led to another problem: if providers charged at average cost for the specialty, or disease type, then more sophisticated procedures, or procedures, say, in teaching hospitals, might become financially untenable. Yet if actual cost to the particular institution were charged, no efficiency incentive would exist, given that for a long time contracts would be placed to reflect existing provision. The alternatives were politically and logistically intolerable. Only in the long term could expensive provision be eschewed by purchasers placing their contracts elsewhere, using a gauge of average or reasonable cost by which to decide how to assess actual prices, related to costs, offered in the marketplace.

Thus, if services are to be contracted to reflect existing provision, both average and actual costs have awkward incentives. The former might render specialist/high-cost institutions untenable; the latter does not encourage efficiency. Admittedly, if contracts are based on market competition, then actual costs – if used as the basis for pricing – can allow purchasers to choose on grounds of cost and other factors. Regulation might be needed to prevent the cheap option always being chosen. In open markets, using average costs to determine prices, by regulation, would not allow price competition, but could allow providers to try to minimize cost given their known prices. But here, as with all the other options, safeguards are necessary.

Every option requires either safeguards for providers and quality, or to ensure that efficiency and incentives are not ignored. Table 5.1 sets this out.

Table 5.1 Contracts to reflect

	Existing provision	**Pattern of provision determined by market**
Regulated pricing (Average cost pricing)	*Advantage* Forces expensive providers to economize.	*Advantage* Incentive to minimize cost, knowing price and revenue (determined to be at average cost).
	Disadvantage Threatens high quality or specialization.	*Disadvantage* No price competition (precluded by regulation); threatens high quality, or specialization.
Free pricing	*Advantage* Protects providers.	*Advantage* Allows purchaser choice on grounds of cost and other criteria.
	Disadvantage No efficiency incentive.	*Disadvantage* Bias to 'cheap and nasty' in practice.

It is interesting to note the effect of seeking to encourage competition among providers, yet regulating prices. If reimbursement is standardized, whether at average cost or marginal cost pricing, then providers will seek profit by minimizing costs, given an expected revenue, rather than trying to boost revenue. If purchasers seek to get a surplus by diminishing referrals to secondary care, then there may be incentives to under-treat. This is in essence the logic behind GP fundholders, who are increasingly seeking to try their hands at the hospital's business. While such innovation has its good points, the dangers must not be overlooked.

There was no necessary relation between overall resource allocation to districts as purchasers, and the likely purchasing prices these districts would pay in contracts. Pre-White Paper, innovative and promising schemes to reconcile revenue allocation and planned provision had existed. Now we were back to confusion and lack of co-ordination.

Making streamlined general management accountable for providing integrated district services was also no longer possible. For example, it might be important to plan integrated care for patients pre-hospital; in hospital; and after discharge in the community; or linking out-patient care with community care, to give but two examples. Now, all these units of care would be financially and organizationally separate. Was it really efficient or sensible to contract for packages of care involving myriad negotiation? Was it not better to build on the logic of many previous NHS reforms and reorganization, and integrate? Full circle ahead to pre-NHS fragmentation was how many people saw things.

Why manage competition when a better alternative had already existed, only to be discredited and removed by a tightly knit group of ideologically motivated men and women?

Introducing competition

The process of moving towards 1 April 1991, the alleged D-day for the NHS reforms, was a frenetic one. This is not in itself a condemnation, for worthwhile reforms may be difficult to establish. In practice, however, significant worries arose over guaranteeing desired outcomes through contracts. Most management time went on the mechanics of change rather than on the outcome of change. Insufficient lead as to outcome, quality, and equity was provided by the Department of Health. The new management executive, understandably, was busy enough with self-governing hospitals, capital charges, and contracting ground rules (NHS Management Executive, 1990).

Worries about adequate funding of research and teaching hospitals' costs were partially attended to, but with a broad brush approach which left out important details. For example, moves towards a new appointment of a chief of research and development, to straddle both health services research and management priorities, failed adequately to define the rôle of research or its independence from day-by-day political and management priorities.

All in all, there was a need to make sense of a radical agenda, which long-time health commentator and former secretary of the Nuffield Trust, Gordon McLachlan, saw as alien to the culture of the British NHS and destructive of many of its achievements (McLachlan, 1990).

In practice, management had to spend most of 1990 'turning current service provisions into contract specification', to quote from the resignation statement of Dr Elaine Murphy, General Manager of Lewisham and North Southwark District Health Authority, on 18 May 1990 (The *Guardian*, 18 May 1990). She was disillusioned at the side-lining of key policy challenges of waiting-lists, inadequate services, and low quality in order to concentrate on the nuts and bolts of contracting.

Perhaps more alarming for the long term was an increasing awareness that purchasers of health care (districts) would not have enough power *vis-à-vis* providers to ensure that patients' and populations' needs, even when adequately defined could be translated into provision. It is fair comment that pre-White Paper, district priorities may often not have been implemented by providers and clinicians, with their own agendas and interests, but the new system was not necessarily an improvement.

Where GPs were to hold their own budgets for mostly elective hospital care, there was tentative evidence they were likely, if influential, to have enough clout as purchasers to distort or divert district priorities as the other purchasers. GPs also were likely to merge into mega-purchasers, and districts, with lower budgets as regions top-sliced money for the GPs' purchasing funds, might find that global, geographical priorities were challenged in a fragmented, pluralistic purchasing system. Even some of the most zealous on the Prime Minister's Review had incidentally worried at this, arguing for competitive provision yet unified purchasing.

GPs might favour hips and production-line treatment as a priority, whereas districts might have preferred other priorities, including prevention and promotion.

Community care, unless provided through ring-fenced budgets, might not be adequately financed. In consequence, hospital care would be further stretched as beds were blocked due to inadequate community care. Sir Roy Griffiths had argued for ring-fencing of money in his proposal that local authorities act as purchasers of community care from a variety of providers. But the government, despite reverses in the House of Lords, was unwilling to guarantee this. Again, a failure to look at the big picture, to focus only on one variable at a time, was detrimental to the overall effectiveness of policy.

Introducing competition was also raising fears as to how far people might have to travel for care in the internal market. Enthoven had originally seen the market as a means for London's great teaching hospitals to raise cash by selling themselves, although ironically their higher prices might militate against this; but apart from this he had not advocated a radical policy involving distant travel to care. Indeed, on economic grounds, contracts might reinforce local provision, unless in exceptional circumstances. But there was no clarity provided.

For market logic might or might not imply significant travel to care. Given so many imponderables, such as the effect of capital charges on different providers in different locations, no one could tell whether or not purchasers would be allowed to include travel costs in an economic evaluation of alternatives; and whether existing services, being already established, could always undercut new developments. After all, a prerequisite of an efficient market was low barriers to entry by providers. Was this the case?

Safeguards for purchasers – and providers

There was a growing determination on the part of the Department of Health in late 1989 and 1990 that when the new system for allocating resources began in April 1991, districts did not find themselves with less money for their residents, i.e. allocations to districts as purchasers, than in the previous year. The political as well as managerial concern with this is not difficult to understand. The Department's communication EL(90)MB/22 asked regions to ensure that '. . . each District, on becoming a purchaser of health care on behalf of its resident population, will open its account in a position at least to continue to provide health care at the level which that population have enjoyed. . . '

The current expenditure on a district's residents, whether on services currently provided within the district or not, had to be maintained. This did not mean there were no districts that would lose in the allocation process, but it did mean that any losses ought to be as a result of allocation being made to purchasers for the district's residents rather than to providers for whatever their catchment population was. In other words, losses could result from losing automatic money for cross-boundary flows of patients from outside the district into the district, but not from less implied expenditure on the district's own population.

There was a key problem here, as indeed with the resource allocation system (RAWP) before the White Paper. If regions were to allocate resources by formulae which reflected need in a manner analogous to the new national formula, but not necessarily the same, then there would eventually have to be gainers and losers, even considering only expenditure on districts' residents. Targets imply gaining and losing. The district's plea to the regions was that initial post-White-Paper allocations did not reflect these targets. One of the key features of abolishing RAWP had been the abolition of the distinction between targets and current or actual allocations. For good reasons as well as bad, a system of slowly moving from actual to target-allocation was to be necessary. Only a significant increase in NHS expenditure could allow the debate about gainers and losers to become a debate about relative gainers.

Another key problem was the implications for providers. Even if districts had enough money for their residents, there was no guarantee they would spend it on the previously prevailing services and units which provided these services. Thus, providers needed to recoup through the contracting system what they had previously been funded for directly, as providers being funded for their catchment populations.

There are arguments for and against this, but here the concern is an additional one. If, for example, a purchasing district wanted to continue to buy services for its population in the same hospitals as before, the continuing viability of those providing institutions might depend on continuing to attract other business – the business, treating cross-boundary flows from other districts, for which they had previously been reimbursed by RAWP. If this did not happen, purchasers might find themselves unable to deal with crippled providers, who could not cover their costs. We are essentially dealing with the economic concept of fixed costs; if a lot of costs are fixed, there is less flexibility to reduce or expand provision; hospitals, for example, may not be very suitable items to trade in a provider market.

The knock-on effects could be substantial. There might be pressure on other providers as a result to take more business than they could handle. Contracts might be impossible to meet; providers might cut corners; purchasers might have to reduce quality demands expressed in the contract.

If GPs used their budgets for certain types of hospital care for elective surgery, further problems for purchasers would emerge. Previously this money was held by districts or regions. If GPs referred for elective surgery, they might merely be referring to a long waiting-list. What this meant was that the district was spending its limited money on other services. Now, however, GP budgets could ensure that the money went on elective surgery. As a result there would not be as much purchasing money for other priorities – all the services previously funded would not be possible, as providers would not get the money.

Fragmentation in purchasing power could therefore seriously affect district priorities. To enforce these requires a global or single purchaser. GP practices forming consortia could become a powerful splinter group at the very least. That is another of the reasons why districts were pushed by some of their parent regions to form purchasing consortia: to try to keep market power as against monopolistic providers and alternative purchasers.

Consortia

The consequence of purchasers of health care, the districts, having to ensure good value from providers is, that the purchasers are increasingly merging into larger purchasing consortia. Whether or not districts formally merge, and many already have done so, this will mean that in practice the distinction between a planning strategy and a competitive strategy is blurred.

Large districts may be considered to be mini-regions. Such organizations will be placing contracts with providers over a wider geographical area within their boundaries. The logic is clear: competition in purchasing is diminished to help ensure that provider competition is not stymied by providers' ability to manipulate purchasers. In the US, pluralism in purchasing ensures that costs are driven up and providers are able to shop around for consumers rather than always vice-versa. Yet a central result will be to ensure that providers are not so free to sell anywhere; by and large there will be planned strategies of provision within fairly self-sufficient mega-districts. This will produce analogies with regional strategic-planning approaches, albeit on a smaller scale and conducted in the rhetoric of competition and contracting.

Markets and alternatives for inter-district charging

Following the Prime Minister's Review of the NHS, the White Paper focused on the provision, rather than the financing, of health services. However, the allocation of resources is likely to provide a major headache both in the short and long term as a result of its recommendations.

Resources will still be given to regions and districts according to a formula based on population weighted by need. After 1991, however, regions were given their actual target allocations, and, it was believed, districts would be moved to their target allocations more quickly than envisaged in the RAWP approach, which existed from 1976–89. A consequence of this will be that funds will not be allocated to districts from regions, such that districts' work for patients in other districts is accounted for in the formula. Instead, districts will have to trade with each other directly for such patients.

A pragmatic approach, combining elements of strategic planning at the regional level, it was thought, would be replaced by an approach which gives budgets for their resident populations, but no more and no less, to districts. If existing flows of patients are not replicated, some districts will find themselves with dramatically reduced budgets and others with enhanced budgets, which may provide a very inefficient result. Districts with reduced budgets may not be able to provide cost-effective health care only for their own populations, as they have been used to providing large-scale services for a wide range of patients from other districts as well, especially the London teaching hospitals. Districts which suddenly find themselves better off may develop services out of the ethic of self-sufficiency, where it would be better to continue to use existing services elsewhere.

Thus, the internal market approach, which depends on giving districts their target allocations quickly, may produce its exact opposite – a boost to district self-sufficiency. That is why abandoning regional strategic planning, because it is part of an outdated philosophy, and replacing it with market trading between districts may be a policy not only fraught with difficulty, but also with irony in that the opposite effect of what is intended may well be achieved.

By August 1989 the unpalatable consequences of the White Paper's recommendations were being exposed and the Secretary of State was back-tracking in order to ameliorate distasteful political consequences. By January 1990 regions were planning districts' cross-boundary flows to prevent political and policy disaster.

The planning alternative

The essence of a planning approach based at the regional level is that sub-regional resource allocation to districts may be bypassed or removed altogether. Resource allocation will instead be dependent upon plans costed according to priorities. Planned need may depend on factors, such as morbidity and social deprivation, which are considered to imply a need for services.

Purchaser–provider confusion: the key elements

District health authorities in practice still have the responsibility of closing facilities and opening new facilities – providers will not be autonomous of purchasers. Regional closure programmes and new developments are progressing in tandem with the implementation of the White Paper, as if the new distinction did not apply.

Contracts with oneself, by districts contracting with their own directly managed units, are contracts only in name. In practice they are merely a new linguistic framework for direct provision using allocated resources, albeit with a new management framework to reflect an alleged purchaser–provider split. Mushrooming managerial bureaucracy may be the order of the day.

Another key reason for being suspicious about the split between purchasing and provision in order to instil wider competition, lies with the control of the medical profession. After the implementation of the White Paper, regions still hold consultants' contracts, but they are managed by districts. Are not the providers to be the marketplace actors, hiring their staff or making contracts with doctors for sessions, as in the US – doctors who may as now work on more than one site? If so, providing units (hospitals and other provider units) ought to employ doctors, either full or part-time. But in practice districts and regions will control medical manpower.

Either doctors will continue to have the major input into deciding use of medical time, or the new contracts will enforce managerial priorities. In the former case, however, contracts by workers will merely reflect provider practice, just as district contracts, in another sense, have to reflect GPs' wishes despite the rhetoric of economically based choice. In the latter case, purchasers may force providers to meet their requirements by acting as providers (employers), as well as purchasers, themselves. Either way, the purchaser–provider split is a myth. The new arrangements may well reflect tighter management of doctors' obligations and time; to dress this up in the language of competition is an unnecessary distinction.

In the US, the policy of regulating costs by reimbursing providers for DRGs at set rates has been described as both a pro-competitive and a planning measure, depending on the perspective of the commentator. If pro-competitive, the DRG policy is only so in that it encourages providers to make a surplus by providing at lower than the standard cost. The same will apply here. In practice, the provider-markets policy in Britain will be an aid to management in planning services at low cost, not a pro-competitive policy.

In Britain, given the low percentage of GDP spent, the aim is to ensure low-cost health care. This means planning within a context of a single, global purchaser of health care. Emulating competitive countries where there are many types of providers and many purchasers (e.g. insurance funds) would in effect mean emulating expensive and barely competitive health care.

New hospitals and new services

Another dilemma of 1990, prior to the implementation of the White Paper, concerned regions' plans for capital programmes. In the future, would they have any right to plan future services, and provide capital moneys accordingly? Or would it now be up to autonomous units, whether self-governing or directly managed, to sell themselves in the marketplace?

In theory, the latter; in practice, seemingly the former. For even if hospitals and other units of service were to manage their own affairs (autonomy, in the case of self-governing trusts; decentralized decision-making within health authorities, in the case of directly managed units), they would still need access to capital if they were to expand or be refurbished. Who would provide this? The answer, seemingly, was to be the regions, acting as banker.

Capital charging

Capital charging was introduced into the NHS following the White Paper of 1989. Capital charging is an attempt to ensure that resources are accounted for, and that these resources include capital as well as recurrent costs. For example, when you buy something in a shop, the price you pay will generally reflect at least the total cost of production. That cost includes not only the salaries of workers and other recurrent costs, but the costs of constructing and refurbishing the factory, or capital costs.

So what, in a hospital context, does capital charging mean? The first challenge is to determine what is capital. Capital is by and large the stock of buildings, infrastructure, and equipment which the health service possesses – theoretically, everything from the hospital itself and the land in which it is situated, to the chair in the DGM's office. Naturally, when accounting for assets in order to implement capital charging, trivial items will not be included.

Why charge? There are two reasons for capital charging. Firstly, the argument is that people or authorities who use capital – land, buildings, or assets generally – ought not to consider it a free good otherwise they will not use it efficiently and effectively. If capital is provided free of charge, there will be no rational choice available as to how to spend limited resources. For example, if money is available in the abstract, it may be an open question as to whether it is used for recurrent budgets or for capital budgets. To put it in policy terms, should one construct one's own hospital using money from capital, or buy services from already existing hospitals elsewhere, using money from recurrent budgets? It is argued that a rent ought to be paid on capital. This is one of the two elements of capital charging.

Secondly, capital depreciates over time; in physical terms a building deteriorates. So money has to be gradually put aside in accordance with accounting principles to ensure that replacement can occur at the end of the day. Depreciation monies can be used for this purpose: the assumed life of an asset, perhaps 50 years, is the time over which depreciation occurs. By the end of that time, one should have enough money to replace the asset.

These two elements of the capital charge are added together to make the total capital charge. The next question is, who levies the capital charge in the health service, and who pays it? The answer to the second question has been more forthcoming: on the one hand, self-governing trusts, and on the other hand, directly managed units (DMUs), will pay capital charges. Working Paper 5 was the first to set out the theory of capital charging. This implied that regions would act as the banker; in other words, regions would levy the charges, receive the money from charges, and therefore bypass districts in this rôle. The logic presumably was that if districts were also, through their DMUs, providers, or to some extent providers as well as purchasers, in their post-White-Paper rôle, it could not be districts who levied charges on themselves.

Working Paper 9 – produced by the Department of Health at the end of 1989 – and a whole series of technical circulars from the Department have given more detail about capital charging. However, the basic operation is still unclear at the time of writing. If, for example, regions are to levy capital charges on existing and new assets, what do they do with the money? The obvious answer is that the money must be redistributed to the service through new projects being financed. In other words, new capital is made available by the banker, the region. This, however, opens a number of policy questions beyond the mere technicalia of capital charging. If regions are to play this rôle, and are to control investment funds, then they will perhaps have a much more significant planning rôle than the theory of the White Paper would envisage.

It could be argued that regions, like any prudent banker, will only provide investment in services which have proven their market-worth or proven their prospective market-worth through a business plan. In practice, however, this theory is likely to be usurped by politics. On a purely economic reading of how capital markets will operate in the NHS, it could be argued that districts which are successful in achieving contracts or ensuring their likelihood of achieving contracts will be able to secure funds for investment. In practice, all sorts of pressures will lead to decisions one way or another.

There is a lot of confusion around the basic concepts of capital charging. One way of ironing out some of the fundamental confusion is to use the White Paper's distinction between purchasing and providing.

In purchasing terms, funds will flow from the Department of Health to the regions, and then to the districts as purchasers, much as before. This does not mean that the formulae are as pre-White Paper, but that the mechanism by which public-sector funds are made available to the NHS is similar. On the purchasing side, monies come for revenue purposes from the Department to regions, and then to districts as purchasers; capital monies also come from the Department to regions. There is an argument for unifying capital and revenue funds to leave it up to regions and districts to decide how to spend the money, but that is a separate argument.

It is on the provider side that the new system comes into operation. Once funds have been made available, capital charges will have to be paid by providing units. This money moves in a circular flow, as it will eventually come back to these units. So purchasing funds percolate through the system as before. It is when these funds are used to purchase services, for example, by districts from providing units, that capital charges are taken into account in calculating the price. In other words, the price of an operation or any other 'good' for sale in the marketplace will have the capital costs and revenue costs of running the enterprise, just like the price of a bar of chocolate contains all the cost components of its production.

Before the distinction between purchasing and provision was drawn, what existed in the health service was simply monies covering both capital and revenue being made available from the centre to the regions and to the districts, and that money then being translated into provision by the districts and their units: there is no conceptual or practical separation of purchasing and providing in the way there is post-White Paper. Costs, of course, had to cover capital costs, in line with the truism that they are needed to build and refurbish as well as to run facilities. It was simply that there was no purchasing mechanism based on charging principles to make this overt; funds were provided and translated directly into provision on a planned basis, but not necessarily on a micro-costed basis.

Now, districts as purchasers, given that they will be facing costs which include capital costs, will have to have their full capital allocation from region as purchasers. This does not affect the fact that regions will act as bankers on the provision side, gathering in capital charges and recycling the money as loans, or rather investments, to providing units. Thus, the main difference with the pre-White-Paper situation is that, before, regions did not necessarily allocate capital right down to districts, but indulged in regional planning and specification as to how capital was to be used, with a lot of top-slicing of capital. After the White Paper, this regional planning rôle will be as a banker to more autonomous providing units, and districts as purchasers will have to have the capital monies on the purchasing side of the equation.

A lot of other questions arise: will capital charging mean that units where land prices are high will be placed at a disadvantage? The Department is already showing signs through its circulars of regulating for this type of eventuality, and things are getting very complex. Will the system operate in practice as intended? Will the outcomes of the policy justify the ferocious amount of confusion and hard work involved?

The wider implications

Regions in practice are likely to continue to plan a region-wide service mix. They hold the purse-strings, in the sense of capital funds for new projects financed out of capital charges. If, however, on the purchasing side they devolve capital funds to districts, they will seemingly be giving up their activist rôle. But this may not be so in practice. They may well provide capital to providing units which seem able to attract contracts, i.e. those which can sell a convincing business plan to their banker.

But contracts themselves will be placed under regional tutelage, even if districts nominally have capital as well as revenue purchasing funds. And even this will not apply in all cases, it seems.

As a result, regions will steer the process. They will advise on contracts and the location of services; provide capital on the supply side, financed from capital charges, now separated from purchasing through contracts which will now reflect capital as well as revenue costs in setting prices; and maybe even provide that capital via districts instead of direct to units.

In practice, purchasing and providing will not really be separated after all. DMUs may be set up organizationally as if they were autonomous from purchasing district health authorities, but in practice districts may simply be using their money to provide services as before, only on paper doing so through contracts for services at prices to include capital costs.

In reality, capital investment may be directly provided from regions via districts to units, with capital charges being nominally levied also by districts on behalf of regions. Thus, capital charges are automatically reimbursed (Figure 5.2) through new investment to units, rather than it being a market process (Figure 5.1), whereby only the total regional income from capital charges (the 'bank's' deposits equates with the total given to units (the 'bank's' lending).

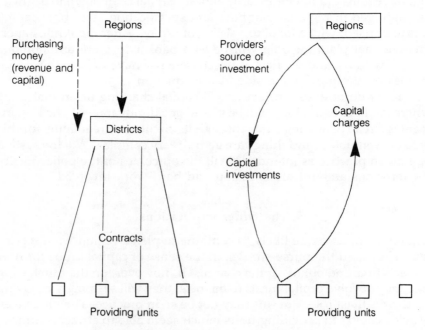

Figure 5.1 Capital charges – market process.

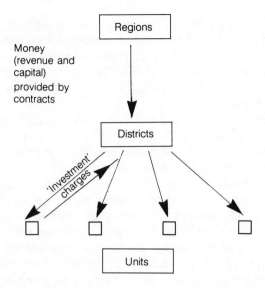

Figure 5.2 Capital charges – automatic reimbursement.

In the restricted version (Figure 5.2), only self-governing trusts (not shown) operate outside the closed planning system. This may well be sensible. But if it is the surreptitiously chosen way, the rhetoric of the White Paper has been responsible for much unnecessary bureaucracy and pretence. As in education and other policy areas, local autonomy may spring from a naïve belief in minimizing unproductive bureaucrats, but consist in increasing them no end. To what extent it is sensible for directly managed units to pretend they are not dependent on a top-down planning process? In practice they will have to employ their own planning, marketing, and costing staff. The purchasers (the parent district; the same organization) will have to replicate all this in order that deals nominally will be done. Is such fragmentation efficient?

Purchasers and providers – the outcome

We have now examined the theory of purchasing and providing, linked to the operation of a competitive market. By spring 1990, Kenneth Clarke was denying that the White Paper was in fact about competition. The government was under pressure from public opinion as well as from the opposition, who had linked the White Paper ideas with privatization and a diminution of the 'NHS as we'd known it'.

Clarke tried to argue that the White Paper was merely about managing resources and priorities through better resource management and information, leading to careful contracts drawn up between purchasers and providers. The result was that a lot of opprobrium came the government's way for their disruptive ideas, yet in practice the implementation of these was to consist largely in dressing up existing and developing practice in the new language. A lot of people had been upset for very little.

Although a market in British health care was increasingly unlikely for both conceptual reasons and now political reasons, the need for purchasers to spell out how NHS districts' priorities were to translate into contracts with providers was still paramount.

Here, another problem arose. Most of the bullish managers wanted to be chief executives of self-governing trusts or directly managed consortia of units. District general managers of often amalgamated and enlarged districts did not always have the capacity or back-up to analyse the need for care and to contract for services accordingly. In practice, providers began to distort purchasers' priorities. The market was in fact an amalgam of provider power and attempts at planning by the new super-districts. The latter were not so much looking for competitive suppliers with whom to place contracts or not as for planned provision within their boundaries. But the weakness of public health medicine, at least as linked to management, in the NHS, despite the Acheson Committee Report of 1988 which advocated a beefing-up of public health, meant that a potential source of information and clout was untapped. Next, in stipulating the mix of objectives in placing contracts, neither government nor health authorities had clear strategies.

Was quality or quantity to win when the two clashed? Was the NHS to be a factory of low-cost but high-quantity operations and services, to try to meet demand? Or a higher-quality service, facing resultingly harder choices within limited budgets?

This had implications for new investment: providers would not incur high capital charges from new capital if purchasers were not willing to pay for this through high enough prices, which in the new system were to reflect both recurrent and capital costs as in any marketplace.

Would resource management be a threat to quality? Or would it aid quality, as only appropriate things were done? Would quality strategies affect the prospects for resource management? Or would a search for quality aid a search for resource management, as the desirable aided the economic: for example, as the need to avoid shoddy services and the prospect of the patient being re-admitted centrally cut the costs of readmission?

Nobody really knew. There were too many complex incentives at work within the new system. For example, if the policy of capital charging led to a real rôle for the region as a banker, would providing units be freer to decide their own strategy *vis-à-vis* quality or quantity? Would regional money for new capital be paid on the basis of respectable business plans by providers reflecting a mix of objectives? Such money was to be paid for by capital charges levied on units, thus completing a circular loop; no new money was involved. The units would recoup the money from purchasing districts, which would now receive all their revenue and capital money via regions from the Department of Health. This was similar to before, except for a greater devolution of the capital side of what was now a purchasing budget.

Or would regions merely see where districts wanted to place contracts, indeed steer them so to do, and finance the units so favoured with capital investment needs merely through the district, obviating the need for a proper capital market separate from provision?

In the end, a messy compromise had to be managed by Clarke, doing his best to rescue things against a sceptical public opinion. Purchasing and provision were formally separated, but merely in order to monitor costs more, not to institute a brave new world of market efficiency. The basic plus of the White Paper – relating income of providers to their workload – could easily have been achieved through a less bureaucratic system of flexible planning. The basic minus of the White Paper, institutionally rationing, as the money followed the patient yet the patient's referral was controlled, still stood.

With all the need for bureaucratic special-reserve funds to ensure contracts were met and patient demands with highly media profile were paid, there would be less money for actual patient care unless the government provided more.

Add to this the government's increasing fear that new regional formulae for allocating resources would as in the old system lead to heavy gainers and losers, and a resulting stipulation, though a Department letter of February 1990, that districts' residents must, in 1991, not suffer a net loss of expenditure on them. The upshot was a regulation of the implementation of the White Paper to a point of contradiction and immobility – partly from a need to 'mend the boat while sailing', due to the hastiness of the implementation; partly due to political fears leading to cobbled-up policy.

Add also the heavy gainers and losers as districts now go to budgets for their resident population, not the services provided – wherever the patients come from, as in the old system – and you had massive uncertainty as to income from formerly directly funded providers. Coupled with self-governing trusts and separate GP funds, this led to a chronic inability to plan for the future – not market efficiency in practice.

All in all, a silly way to make policy: it is known that, only days and weeks before the White Paper was published in early 1989, individuals and think-tanks were being asked desperately for advice as to key recommendations and structures. This reflected the Prime Minister's binning of earlier, more judicious, drafts.

Another worrying aspect of conviction policy made on the hoof is the need to ensure that health service managers are evangelists rather than at least partly independent actors. Throughout the 1980s, and accentuated by the Review, a diminution in the scope for managers to express criticism of policy and implementation has been marked. Only those managers who have alternative power bases could speak out. There is an alarming discrepancy between the opinions of managers in public and those expressed in private. Is this a sensible, let alone democratic, way to run a public service? Is the philosophy of 'one of us or you're out' to be extended indefinitely? An editorial in the *Health Service Journal* (10 May 1990) suggested the acuteness of this issue, in showing how critical comment was under threat.

Later plans for a task force acting from the Department of Health to manage news from potential media trouble-spots, in October 1991, also suggested an obsession with whitewash.

The implementation of the White Paper's recommendations: politics and the art of the possible

It is hardly surprising that different actors, inside and outside government, had different agenda and priorities as the White Paper *Working for Patients*, was passed through Parliament via the NHS and Community Care Bill, and, even before its passage, as changes were made in the operation of the NHS in line with the Paper.

Firstly, those who had been most seminal in originating the ideas and proposals at the most general level, such as Professor Enthoven, were either not involved at all, or hardly involved, in the practical follow-up. Once the academics had moved on, the politicians and bureaucrats moved in. Secondly, those ideological crusaders from the various think-tanks had attempted to adapt pro-market ideas for delivering health care to the British situation, but regrettably with little detailed information as to the practical implications for a publicly financed and publicly planned service such as the NHS. They too were peripheral when it came to working out the problems on the ground.

Next, politicians both inside and outside the Cabinet had widely varying degrees of attachment to the proposals within the White Paper. Once it became clear that a significant practical problem existed in implementing them, the exercise became one of damage limitation: it had to be defended as an exciting attempt to transform the NHS of the future, yet at the same time practical problems had to be minimized. This was done by preserving as much as possible of existing NHS practice. The letter but not the spirit, the language but not the real thrust, behind the White

Paper, became the real focus. Within the Department of Health, it was naturally a priority both of the NHS management executive, created from the former NHS management board by White Paper recommendations, without the need for legislation, and also the traditional civil servants in Department of Health divisions, to provide some order out of the impending chaos.

A London factor?

Given higher costs and in particular much higher capital charges if left to the market, some London providers may bluntly be put out of business by the White Paper and its consequences – if the latter are permitted. In other words, if London providers were to sell their services in the marketplace, given costs and prices in London, they might lose out heavily.

This was particularly ironical in that much of the intellectual genesis of the White Paper lay in Enthoven's idea for an internal market within the NHS. Enthoven had seen the internal market primarily as a means of ensuring that specialized providers operating from centres of excellence, in particular London teaching hospitals such as Guy's, St. Bartholomew's, and St. Thomas's, would be able to survive financially. In the old system, such providers had often been situated in districts such as Lewisham and North Southwark, City and Hackney and West Lambeth, which had to cut their spending on services for their resident populations in order to reach their targets; it was alleged in line with the RAWP formula that they had historically been spending too much on their populations.

Quite apart from the fact that this seemed highly untenable to those faced with the twin demands of providing teaching hospitals and services for socially deprived populations, there was a particular analytical problem for the large teaching hospitals.

In order to try and cut its budget, the host district might seek to cut expenditure significantly on the teaching hospitals. The district as a whole might not really be a net importer or exporter of patients: although the teaching hospital might well be a net importer of patients in that it would treat patients from other districts, and in many cases outside London altogether, the rest of the district might well export patients. For example, patients requiring non-teaching hospital care might get it in other districts. Thus, the situation confronting the district and the hospital might not be the same: the district, despite many flows in and out, might find that these balanced each other out, whereas the teaching hospital would likely be a net importer of patients. The RAWP formula, however, had only recompensed the district, not the hospital itself, for such inflows. And such recompense was not necessarily realized in practice as it was the target and not the actual allocation which benefited from imports into the district.

Enthoven and others who developed his proposals into the ideas upon which the White Paper drew, argued that a system of direct charging would benefit hospitals in Inner London such as Guy's and St. Thomas's. They would be able to sell their services directly, without the money either going to the district and never really benefiting the teaching hospital, or the money coming too late and in too small quantities through the RAWP formula. For example, it was argued that specialized services offered by the teaching hospitals were not adequately recompensed by the RAWP formula's system of reimbursing flows from one district to another at national average cost. This has, however, been disputed.

Practical and political consequences

In practice using a market system to pay providers of health care is likely to disadvantage all of London, both teaching and non-teaching hospitals, other than politically favoured self-governing trusts.

Other London institutions might face a bleak future. Department of Health Circular EL(90)MB/22 had admittedly talked of Thames Districts being given purchasing allocations through a resource allocation procedure from regions, which reflected the higher prices of London services. However, 'over time, all non-Thames Districts should move to a weighted capitation based allocation which includes no Thames' allowances'. The import of this was that purchasing districts outside London would find it unattractive to buy expensive London services.

It was suggested that policy-makers have had the diminution of expensive London care as part of a hidden agenda. Attempts in the past to use the planning process to redistribute out of London had foundered on medical opposition and the preponderance of London medical schools. It is now argued in some quarters that markets may be achieving what the planning process could not, as London is squeezed.

A major consequence was likely to be that the system of contracting created by the White Paper would not provide a boost to trading between districts, inside and outside London, as the varying price structures would ensure that districts in Outer London and outside London altogether would seek to develop and pay for their own services rather than to pay for the more expensive London services. Thus, the so-called internal market policy might in fact operate, as districts were given purchasing power for their own residents, with districts trying to provide as much as possible for themselves.

The policy might well achieve its opposite. The fact that districts were increasingly organizing themselves into purchasing consortia, to ensure that purchasers were large enough to have bargaining power *vis-à-vis* providers, and indeed to ensure that inter-district strategically planned service mixes were preserved, would be one factor which could mitigate the parochialism of district self-sufficiency.

How to ration?

If the White Paper is actually about rationing care through contracts which stipulate what types of care can be provided on the NHS, what about theories of rationing which give intellectual respectability to such an approach?

The best known in Britain, although derived from US research, is the Quality Adjusted Life Years (QALY) approach, which seeks to measure how much improvement in health status as well as lengthening of life results from specific procedures. The cost is then applied to the calculation, so that cost-per-QALY can be derived to compare different medical procedures' cost-effectiveness.

In the US, the State of Oregon has recently seen controversy as a result of using an analogous mathematical approach to rationing care for Medicaid patients, drawing on polling by telephone in order to rate priorities.

If rationing is inevitable, doing it formally rather than by back-door means, for example, through waiting-lists where clinicians effectively decide, may seem sensible. But many problems, both practical and ethical, abound. How does one compare a life saved for three years with a life improved for 30 years? Who decides: patients, relatives, doctors, experts or all citizens? What ethical imperatives concerning life cannot be transgressed, if any?

A political objection is that such approaches institutionalize rationing. It is significant that Medicaid (poor) patients in the US and those patients unable to go private in the UK would be the worst hit by such a policy – if the policy ruled out their necessary treatment on grounds of cost-effectiveness. Some rationing may be inevitable. But gung-ho experts ought to beware giving comfort in their enthusiasm for rationing games to those who wish to restrict public care while allowing waste in the private sector. Those who say 'the latter is not wasting public money' take a partial and essentially individualistic approach to society's resources.

Doctors in a public system will tend to oppose QALYs, partly because they fear analytical means of subverting disorganized clinical autonomy, but also because they sensibly fear half-baked and ethically dubious enthusiasms.

The White Paper seeks to replace limited back-door rationing with more widespread overt contracting for stipulated services. It is only a short step to employing QALYs, or analogous approaches, to decide what need is to be met, and why.

Contracting may bring some efficiency improvements in ensuring that purchasers decide rationally what to buy on behalf of their populations, but the sinister side of the coin ought not to be blithely ignored.

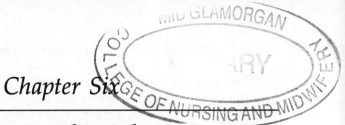

Chapter Six

Management, political economy, and health policy

THE MANAGEMENT OF THE NATIONAL HEALTH SERVICE – POLITICS AND POLICY

Political science has devised concepts which describe the location of power in institutions and in political society as a whole. Pluralism connotes a situation in which power is spread or shared, and in which policy is not dominated by élites, even if it is not distributed equally. This should not be confused with devolution of power. Centralized power can be shared, as in Britain, when things work well, by comparison with the US's decentralized politics. Similarly, devolved power can lead to a situation in which policy is dominated by élites. That is, debates about degrees of pluralism and élitism, its opposite, can be distinguished from debates about centralism and devolution (for example, national domination of policy versus federally spread or locally influenced policy). As well as pluralism and élitism, Marxism and other variants of class theory can be posited. Likewise, other perspectives on power exist (Paton, 1990).

It should be noted that these terms are descriptive, not prescriptive. One can be an élitist in this sense yet deplore the fact that élites dominate policy. One can be a political Conservative and accept a Marxist or radical analysis which posits an economically based ruling class, and approve of that state of affairs.

Regarding the NHS, there have been long debates about who makes health policy (Ham, 1985), and who controls the levers of power within the NHS: that is, in implementing policy (Klein, 1989). It was widely thought that doctors are a dominant élite for some time. Following Alford (1975), rationalizing moves to corporate management, called general management in recent NHS parlance, are seen as the supplanting of one élite – a professional élite, the medical profession – with another – a management élite. So why has the Conservative Party supported the bureaucrats against their natural ally, the doctors? It seems that the strict control of public money provides the answer. That is why general management – in many ways a useful mechanism for enforcing social priorities in a complex service dominated by professions and interest-groups – has been distrusted by the left. It makes sense, nonetheless, for Labour to maintain it, yet strip it of its right-wing, anti-worker, anti-public expenditure context and connotations.

In the 1980s the Conservatives diminished the independence of health authorities, of the NHS professions and staff, and of all lines of advice and control which cut across the direct politically managed line which is supposed to enforce Ministers' preferences. Consider the pre-general management (pre-Griffiths) hierarchy in the health policy arena, to see the complexity which the Conservatives thought needed to be sorted out (Figure 6.1).

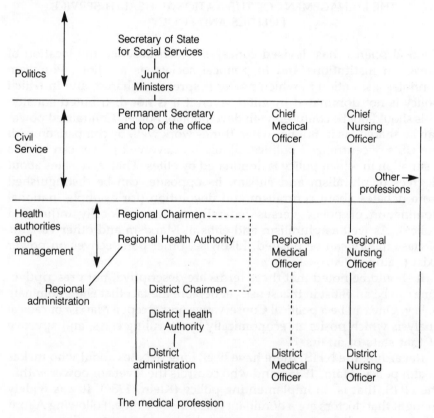

Figure 6.1 Pre-general management hierarchy

The 1983 Griffiths Inquiry sought to impose hierarchical general management to replace consensual administration both in the NHS and at the centre (Figure 6.2).

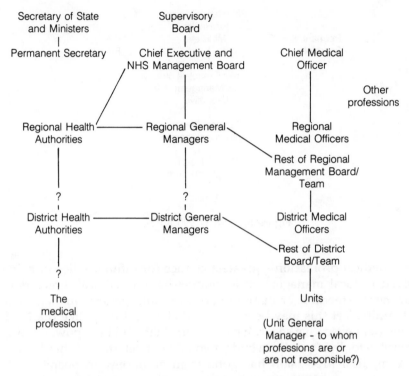

Figure 6.2 Hierarchical general management.

The White Paper's management prescriptions were born in the confusion caused by the Griffiths saga. Were district health authorities now responsible to regions, in a chain up to the centre and the management board? What about the professions? Were they now responsible to general managers? What about the Permanent Secretary? And so on. Thus, the post-1990 NHS was intended to be as seen in Figure 6.3.

Health authorities, professions, and the national civil service are subservient, it seems, to the political/managerial spine of the NHS. Health authorities are now business boards, not representative or quasi-representative of their communities. The irony here is that the safety-valve function of the local health authority in absorbing criticism is now likely to go. The White Paper was about passing the buck from the Secretary of State to local management, but political blame now has an obvious route: upwards to the Secretary of State and government! If local hospitals close, if funds are inadequate, everyone knows power has been centralized, even if responsibility has been decentralized, and so everyone knows who to blame. Outcomes do not always follow intentions.

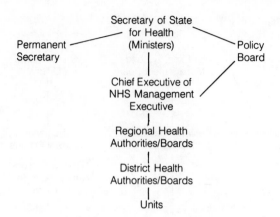

Figure 6.3　Post-1990 NHS.

The medical profession's greatest chance for influence lies in being involved in local management as budget-holding clinical directors of departments (medical or operational) or as unit general managers of whole units. Yet this may be a poisoned chalice if they, like the NHS management executive so far, have responsibility but little power. Being responsible for living within a budget you do not determine is hardly fun.

The medical profession has gone from autonomy in hospitals, as between 1948 and 1974, through a variety of managerial fixes, back to a kind of autonomy as directors of departments and even general managers. Yet the new autonomy is at the cost of shouldering the burden of rationing care, within, albeit not between, specialties.

It makes sense to involve doctors in management at the specialty level rather than automatically at the overall hospital/provider level or health-authority level. In other words, the 1974 reorganization did some damage in removing medical influence from, and centralizing, planning. Coming full circle, only now with management by clinicians in the context of resource awareness, may not be a bad thing. But allying the new policy with cuts, or promising flexibility and devolved management plus devolved financial control without delivering, is potentially disastrous.

THE WHITE PAPER: COMPARISON WITH OTHER PRO-COMPETITIVE POLICY

The law

The Courts and Legal Services Bill of 1990 sought to diminish professional power, in this case, the monopoly of barristers in the higher courts. In this respect there is an analogy with the White Paper's philosophy of diminishing the power of professional providers. In the case of the legal reforms, however, the absence of equity in ability to purchase legal services, unlike the relatively egalitarian NHS, means that reforms affecting providers cannot be expected to benefit the public generally.

Reforms limiting the monopoly of private providers of legal services may, however, be more worthwile than attempts to subject NHS doctors, who do not constitute a private monopoly, to the discipline of working for competing health-care providers. Forcing health care into a competitive model may lead to the loss of the altruism and service ethic which helps to inspire a publicly provided health service. Patients may have less chance of free referral without economic considerations being paramount if public purchasers have to justify their contracts with providers. In the legal arena, however, private purchasers are bound to seek the most economic services consistent with their preferences. Restrictions on free access, e.g. to expensive barristers, as a result of pro-competitive laws may be a cost of ensuring that affordable legal packages are available, at least more widely if not generally, as a result of competitive forces in provision. In an arena such as health, where equity is established, however, restricting access to some on grounds of economy is less justifiable.

Education

Schools competing for parents' choices, with or without changes, and universities competing for students may have sensible elements. Just as the internal market in health may lead, however, to purchasers being subservient to providers, competition in education may disadvantage some purchasers. Providers who prosper may not seek the custom of 'poor' or 'difficult' consumers.

The policy of competition has different empirical arguments for and against in different policy areas. Overall, some elements of the philosophy are the same. This is hardly surprising, as the ideology of the Thatcher governments argued for such an approach. Yet there was a failure to distinguish more reasonable applications of competition, where the alternative was private monopoly, from the less reasonable, where planned, public provision was a superior alternative, from the viewpoint of equity and efficiency, as in the NHS, or where competition was not possible, as in various utility privatizations. Even those who ideally choose public provision may sometimes choose competition as the lesser of private evils. Yet the 1980s governments allied competition to a dogma of privatization and private administration of public services wherever possible. In this context, suspicion of the NHS reforms was neither surprising nor unreasonable.

What about the suspicion of conspiracy – that the White Paper was about weakening the NHS and ripening it for privatization? In itself, it is not. Yet some advisers close to Mrs Thatcher in the late 1980s saw the removal of the NHS as an eventual priority in a fourth term. The problem for such zealots in 1987–9 was that the radical agenda in other policy areas forced a limited kind of pragmatism on the Prime Minister. Replacing the NHS with largely private insurance was too daunting, and unpopular, a task. After all, even the poll-tax had only been pushed through at the cost of complex amendments, guaranteeing unpopularity yet an absence of efficient result even by government criteria.

In the future, the NHS could be weakened by further giving incentives for private care through the tax system; by preventing its growth (by international standards it is already significantly under-funded) such that people, firms, and organizations increasingly go private; by demoralizing its key staff; and, by introducing such complexity in the name of efficacy that the NHS's real advantages, for example, low administrative costs, are in the end lost. Prime Minister John Major set out a major commitment to the NHS in late 1991 by comparison with his predecessors. But the forces for greater private-sector activity in the long run are strong. Affluent societies prefer to spend money privately than publicly, even if the latter is a more efficient route in health. The Labour Party is genuinely more popular on health matters; but health is only one factor at a general election.

It is widely believed on the left of politics that the governments of the 1980s saw general management and all its agenda of efficiency savings as part of a strategy to ensure that expenditure on the NHS was tightly constrained.

New right, or for that matter, old right, politics called for cuts in the welfare state. The logic is that the private, capitalist, economy requires low social spending, to allow adequate private investment and incentive. Interestingly, neo-Marxists endorse this, but add that welfare spending is necessary to legitimize capitalism throughout society. Thus, a fiscal crisis arises as taxes are cut to provide private incentive, yet expenditure mounts – on the welfare state; on the infrastructure of the economy; and, indeed, on government subsidies to the private sector.

The left-wing solution is socialism. The right-wing solution, crudely put, is to cut across the board; the right-wing solution, subtly put, is to cut selectively. Popular institutions such as the NHS can be preserved if modified and restricted; less popular or divisive programmes, such as housing for the poor, can be cut. Overall, the fiscal crisis is solved by getting society to acquiesce, i.e. maintaining legitimacy, in lower levels of government activism in the social sector. It is both an ideological and economic project.

Broadly, the latter has occurred. Expenditure on the NHS, while maintained, has to be constrained. Hence the whole panoply of initiatives in the 1980s, some of which pre-dated Griffiths, is the stress on voluntarism in *Patients First* (1981); the Rayner scrutinies; the government-made value-for-money initiative; performance indicators as a stick with which to beat health managers; more restrictive resource allocation policies; the resource management initiative, following earlier clinical budgeting exercises; and various others.

To these can be added the Griffiths Inquiry itself; the White Paper of 1989; the second Griffiths report on community care; and various initiatives in primary care concerning restricting expenditure on the FPS.

Understood in this context, general management has a neutral rôle to play in meeting health service objectives, but also an ideological rôle as a tool of the government's perspective. The importing wholesale of private-sector language, in a way which surprises even conservative US commentators, is a symptom of how managers feel they have to appeal to their masters. This is not to deny the utility of certain techniques; it is to criticize a lack of selectivity.

The future of private health care

There is an egalitarian argument for encouraging a larger private sector. This goes that the remaining NHS will be able to concentrate on the needier. At present, it is argued, those who benefit those from the NHS are in fact the more articulate, middle-class members of society. The other side of the coin, however, is that the removal on a large scale of these clients from the NHS would remove the most articulate source of practical criticism within the NHS which helps to keep up standards.

Such an argument is also naïve about the future of funding for the NHS. In order that NHS resources be used on the genuinely needy, it would be necessary that funding not be cut in proportion to the diminution of population using it.

Firstly, those likely to move to the greener pastures of private care would tend to be the more affluent, less frequently ill members of society, whose expected use of health resources would be less than average. Therefore, any diminution of money going to the NHS in proportion to diminution of population using it would have to be tempered by the age and expected morbidity of those remaining.

Next, the argument for targeting resources on the needy, by limiting the universality of the NHS, would imply a significant increase in resources. While this is possible in the abstract, there is a compelling reason why public finance for such an NHS would not be forthcoming on the expected scale. Those economically and politically powerful individuals who were no longer dependent on the NHS would find themselves dependent on expensive private care with expensive rivate health insurance. The pressure for tax credits for such insurance, and indeed for lower taxes generally, would be great. This pressure would be quite likely to lead to lower real expenditure on the remaining NHS, even per head of population still dependent upon it.

The arguments for a greater use of private care in Britain have not come from the egalitarian or left wing of the political spectrum. Very much a buzz-phrase of the 1980s has been co-operation between public and private sectors. In 1982 the *Patients First* document stressed reliance on non-statutory sources. The competitive tendering initiative stressed the contribution in the private sector to be great for support services. The private sector has developed, as rationing and waiting-lists, as well as closures due to shortage of finance, have spread throughout the NHS in the mid-1980s. John Moore's 1987 speech to the Conservative Party Conference was the clearest harbinger of a significant pro-private-sector initiative, although couched in generalities. His replacement by Kenneth Clarke put paid to some of these dreams.

It surprised some commentators that the Conservatives did not significantly extend tax credits for private health care prior to the 1989 White Paper. At present, only those with relatively low incomes are eligible for such tax credits. Unlike in the US, where most of one's expenditure on health insurance or health care can be written off to tax, in Britain it is the dominant rôle of the Exchequer in policy-making which has prevented extensions rather than ideological opposition to such extensions. As already described during the early stages of the Prime Minister's Review of 1979, various ideas to allow people either to contract out of the NHS or to receive significant tax credits, or even full rebates of anticipated expenditure on them on the NHS were considered. Political unpopularity was naturally a threat, and in addition the Treasury argued strongly against such policies, the Treasury being influential generally in the Review. The short-term argument used by the Treasury is that what economists call dead-weight loss would be incurred by giving tax credits for private health care: those who already have the private insurance, without receiving the tax credits, would get them. More significantly in the long term, the Treasury is generally not keen to give away current sources of revenue.

In consequence, there was instead a vaguer policy. The buzz-phrase of 'co-operation with the private sector' was part of the standard health service rhetoric in the 1980s. Yet it was generally a misnomer. More significant was competition with the private-health sector: forced into a more entrepreneurial rôle, providers of health care within the NHS have tried to compete with private health care in a way which had gone out of fashion following Barbara Castle's and the Labour government's attempts to remove private health care from NHS hospitals in the mid-1970s. In other words, the NHS will increasingly compete with private providers to provide private health care to the population. Additionally, NHS support services will compete with private concerns to deliver services to the NHS. And in certain markets, NHS services can be supplied through the private sector. In a broad political sense, there may be co-operation; in an economic sense, it is more like competition.

The Conservative Government of the 1980s and early 1990s generally sought to increase the use of private-sector facilities by the NHS. This may not always be a wise policy in the long term: proper option appraisal and cost-benefit analysis would be necessary to decide whether it was better for the NHS to invest in itself for the future or to contract for use of private-sector hospitals, for example, which find themselves with spare capacity due to over-optimistic readings of the future market. Despite its market rhetoric, however, the government, even after the White Paper, is not keen to be liberal in allowing health authorities to behave commercially, not least in borrowing money for the future. Self-governing trusts will, within limits, be able to do so; the rest of the NHS will not.

Certain theorists of both left and right wings in politics have argued that capitalist mixed economies face inevitable fiscal pressures, sometimes dramatized as a fiscal crisis, in seeking to reconcile revenue sources and public expenditure. It is argued on the left that a market economy has to be run with low taxes, but that it needs to spend a lot on the infrastructure of the economy to aid private capital and also on social services to provide legitimation and to cover up for the inequality created. In the more thorough-going capitalist economies, these necessary expenditures are complemented by the fact that public services are provided expensively using private markets. The argument therefore runs that the downward pressure on tax and the upward pressure on expenditure creates a fiscal crisis.

Interestingly, right-wing theorists have put forward a remarkably similar account. They argue that the capitalist economy requires low taxes to provide incentives to individuals; that interest groups and pressure groups put excessive pressure upon the political system to provide them with special benefits which are expensive; and correspondingly that public expenditure becomes too high. If taxes remain low, there is a budget deficit with all the consequences which we have seen recently in a number of Western countries.

While in Britain, the NHS has been significantly more protected than other social services and social policy generally, it has still been operating in a cold climate under a government operating from the basic premise that public expenditure is bad and low taxation is good. Ideological support for the private sector has therefore been inevitable, in that private health care is one step away from expecting the state to deliver through public expenditure.

There are many ethical and political objections to the existence of the private sector at all, if there is any rationing of needed care in the public sector for reasons of unavailablity of resources. Nevertheless, any pragmatic assessment will conclude that a private-health-care sector is not going to disappear in the near future. There are dangers in seeking to incorporate as much provision of private care as possible within the structure of the NHS – not least the danger of inequity for public as opposed to private patients, as doctors and facilities are monopolized for the purposes of revenue generation from private patients by the public sector. Nevertheless, there are advantages as well. If the medical profession is to continue to work in both public and private sectors, greater control and value for money from clinicians may be obtained by having them on-site rather than theoretically delivering NHS care for most of their time and private-sector care for part of their time, yet in practice spending much of their time in the private sector. Another obvious advantage is that the revenue from private care, the more it is conducted within the NHS, will come to the public sector.

The overall problem for public policy is that the more incentives are given to people to become private patients, with the revenue going to the NHS, the more one may end up with a system whereby many people are in fact paying user charges for use of NHS facilities.

THE POLITICAL CONTEXT OF HEALTH POLICY IN THE 1980s

To understand the context of evolving health policy in the 1980s it is necessary to consider Conservative stewardship of the economy in that decade, and to analyse the nature of the electoral coalition which twice returned Mrs Thatcher to power.

Health policy was not responsible for relative Conservative popularity: indeed, the latter persisted despite it, for a number of reasons. The opposition was split; the country did not trust Labour's economic policy; and many people believed Thatcherism represented the good life, speaking economically, when incomes increased, without noticing how work and conditions had changed, quantitatively and qualitatively, for the worse.

Overall economic policy prevented significant public spending on health to keep pace with demography, technology, health-sector inflation, new priorities, and, – most importantly – our European neighbours. 'Sound economic management' was the slogan of the decade.

In assessing Conservative management of the economy, the main focus should be upon longer-term economic and political objectives. It is important to consider to what extent there have been rising standards of living under the Conservatives; the extent to which any increased income or wealth since 1979 is attributable to Conservative policy; the extent to which greater economic output and social achievement comes about only through a disproportionate increase in work intensity (i.e. to explore the relationship between work, leisure, and economic success); and the exent to which families are better off by any well-rounded definition of that term. Naturally, in exploring overall economic output and economic success, distribution also has to be considered: it is important to see the extent to which the fruits of the economy are distributed equitably. In this connection, regional and class differences in benefit from Conservative policies must also be kept in mind.

Economic progress

Despite faster growth rates than our European partners for a short period in the mid-1980s, total economic wealth in Britain did not grow in the Thatcher years faster than in other European countries. Economic growth rates and growth rates in labour productivity can be explained almost wholly by reference to the slump which occurred between 1979 and 1981, during which time economic growth was negligible and unemployment soared to such an extent that labour productivity was simply bound to grow subsequently as a result of the economic truism that the fewer workers that are employed, the greater the average productivity will be.

Unemployment was falling slightly by the end of the decade. It seemed likely that, after adjusting for changes in the rules governing the receipt of state benefit, and for the distribution of jobs into full-time and part-time, and also for international trends, the fall in full-time equivalent unemployment as a result of British government policy was tiny, if positive at all. The regional disparity in the fall of unemployment was also notable. The recession of 1990 onwards reversed even minor benefit.

Increasing removal of health and safety benefits, and increasing exploitation explained the greater attractions to employers of cheap labour, and there was a greater willingness to ignore environmental damage and decay in Britain's infrastructure. Britain effectively adopted a Third World economic strategy.

Definition of economic benefit

Economists since the 1960s have reminded us that GNP is a narrow measure of economic benefit, let alone of social benefit. While there has no doubt been a significant growth in the general availability of various consumption goods and high technology products, there has been a severe decline in the quality of the environment, judged by a number of quite specific criteria. Roads and motorways are now considerably more crowded and journeys are more time-consuming. Cities, public spaces, and the countryside are less attractive as a result of an abrogation of public responsibility in planning, owing to an obsession with letting market forces rip.

The intensity of work for core workers has increased dramatically, in both the shrinking sector of blue-collar jobs and in a variety of white-collar settings, whether in the private sector, in the public and bureaucratic sectors, the health service, or the education sector, including universities. Meanwhile, peripheral workers and the unemployed suffer. As in the US, rising standards of living are only sustainable as a result of more work effort per family unit. In the 1950s it was true as a generalization that the average worker's annual wage was roughly equivalent to the cost of his family house – a worker earning £800 in the 1950s would be able to buy a house in North London for £800. One need only think of an equivalent worker today – perhaps earning £10,000 in London and confronting a price for the same house of £120,000 – to realize the dramatic decline in the real standard of living in this sector. Families may now have two cars; they are also more likely to need two cars. We have here a chicken-and-egg situation: people work in order to have two cars, but they require two cars in order to work and manage the family.

An increasingly mobile society is a society in which leisure time is diminished as the working day is lengthened, for yuppies and white-collar workers especially. The time involved in travelling to work and home again is increased, sharply in the metropolis due to worsened public transport and streets confronting gridlock, New York-style traffic. Groups of workers display Durkheim's primitive solidarity as social responsibility is weakened. The irony is that the more complex and organic economic society becomes, the less organic and the more tribe-like its constituent groups have been encouraged to become.

Overall, the challenges to healthy living are many. The health status of different social classes is widening, not because of the NHS but because other social policies have been diminished, such as public housing; environmental regulation; urban planning, with consequences for health which leave the NHS very much as the social worker fighting the odds on behalf of disadvantaged clients.

The balance sheet

If we consider consumption in the broadest sense, referring to a variety of services and leisure goods, as well as traditional consumer goods, we have a very unclear picture as to economic progress in recent years. Efficiency was a favourite word of the Conservative Government under Mrs Thatcher; efficiency is, however, more evident in word than in deed. The more one broadens the definition of benefit and cost in the economy, the clearer it seems that production of goods and leisure is less efficient because it requires more input proportionate to output, except for the very rich indeed. What is more, dogmatic privatizations, creating private monopolies, produce more costs for many of the workers involved than any benefit they may receive as consumers, or share-owners of tiny consequence.

The ideology of consumption is rampant, and associated with the ideology of the 'loadsamoney' society. The reason for the co-existence of ostentatious wealth, greed, and social irresponsibility, yet worsening conditions in the lower-paid jobs of our society is, however, clear. A balanced society is one in which wealth is shared equitably enough that producers and consumers are by and large the same people: workers produce and spend their reasonably fair wages on consumption. In our society today there is a widening divorce between the world of consumption and the world of production. On the one hand owners, managers, and affluent workers who are at the core of the production process, but do not engage in the dirty jobs of production, are the new rampant consumers. On the other hand, there is the increasingly marginalized proletariat and salariat, those who are on low wages and low salaries doing jobs which are at the periphery of the economy, but which are vital for the economy nonetheless.

The health consequences in the long run will doubtless involve growing discrepancies in health status between the affluent majority and the minority who are excluded from both material and cultural participation. Both material and social deprivation are related to ill-health, as much research has suggested.

Whatever language, jargon, or clichés are used, we live in a post-industrial society in which the old majoritarian working class has disappeared. Work places are decentralized and less hierarchical, but there is less work in general. Those who work, work more intensely, while many either do not work at all or work in poorly paid, part-time jobs with virtually no unionization and poor conditions. We see the phenomenon of pockets of ill-health rather than a more old-fashioned graduation between classes, including the extreme case of unemployment-linked morbidity, and even mortality.

Economic gains under Thatcherite conservatism?

The question we have to ask is not who is better off by comparison with 1979, full stop (the answer is nearly everyone in the world, bar the poorest countries of the Third World), but who is better off, by comparison with 1979, than they would have been in the absence of Thatcherite conservatism?

It is clear that very rich and upper-middle classes are better off. This is primarily a result of the changes in tax rates and in the tax system, which has become much less progressive, especially in consequence of the 1988 Budget. Additionally, there is a minority, albeit sizeable, of affluent workers who were certainly as well off, if not better off, under Thatcherism. Business unionism as practised by the EETPU and the Union of Democratic Mineworkers is testimony to the attempt by groups of workers and their leaders to buy in to the fruits of the enterprise culture.

In health care, a consequence is a greater interest in private care and insurance, as a low-tax, low-social-expenditure economy both worsens the prospects for improvements in public services and allows the rich more cash for private consumpton of formerly social benefits. Worryingly, as the economy becomes more differentiated, the mercenary argument for a national health service as an investment in our workers becomes less universally applicable. If health care is in part an investment in human capital, why invest in the redundant minority? Brutally, this is the US position; do we want to reach it?

Clear economic gainers under Thatcherism do not fully explain the political ascendency of the Conservative Party in the 1980s. Of course, it must be kept in mind that the Conservative Party in 1979, 1983, and 1987 obtained approximately 42% of the vote of those who voted, very roughly, 40% of 80%, at the most. This means 32% of those eligible to vote voted for Thatcherite conservatism. Even keeping this in mind, it must still be asked how a coalition to produce majorities of 100 or more for the Conservatives has been put together electorally. One must go beyond pure economic self-interest to understand the voting coalition which produces the Thatcher governments.

Debates between radical thinkers of one school – who point to the ideological dominance of Thatcherism – and their radical counterparts – who point to the new social structure of the society and the encouragement of economic self-interest, often through fiscal subsidies, by the Thatcher government – polarize the argument far too much. For it is the siting of both economic interest and perceived economic interest within an ideological context which produced Conservative dominance.

It has become fashionable to point to the decline of left-wing coalitions in both Britain and the US. In Britain, the prospects for Labour majorities as in 1945, and, to a lesser extent, in 1966, are now seen by both political theorists and psephologists to have receded to the point of near impossibility.

The first point to note about all this is that liberal programmes in the US, and social and economic reforms in Britain are themselves partly responsible for the restructuring of society which has led to the re-emergency of the right: the liberal left has been too successful for its own good, and has put itself out of business. Greater opportunity throughout society has led to a loosening of working-class and various other group loyalties. However, were the welfare state to be abolished completely, then the rationale for its existence would re-emerge. It is notable that in the US, perception of the prosperity in the Reagan–Bush years depends upon a number of crucial assumptions. The only families which see themselves as unequivocally better off are by and large those with a double income, without significant or catastrophic health-care costs, and the confidence that education and university costs for their children will not be passed significantly further back to the individual.

Pragmatism has compelled Republican administrations to maintain fiscal subsidy for the middle classes where it is politically necessary – socialism for the better off, if you like. Similarly, in Britain, Mrs Thatcher balanced her ideological attacks on the welfare state with fierce, if selective, defence of welfare for the middle classes, and electoral bribery for the affluent working classes.

Plans to privatize the NHS were put on the back burner in 1981–2, and dusted off again with more, although strictly limited, success in 1988. The full panoply of middle-class subsidies, such as mortgage tax relief, especially relief from the higher band of taxation, has been maintained. Council houses have been sold at knock-down prices to sections of the working class. There has been an attempt to involve groups of workers in share purchase.

In Britain also the free market and the enterprise society have been accompanied by centralized political manipulation to assemble and maintain right-wing electoral coalitions to replace liberal-left coalitions, as witnessed earlier in the century.

The right-wing coalition

Even such economic measures and incentives, however, are not enough. As well as those who had an economic interest in Thatcherism in the short term, there are those who think they have an economic interest in Thatcherism as it lives on after its namesake has gone. This is where ideology, and in some cases pure deception, comes in. A share-owning mentality is imparted to those who may nevertheless lose a lot more through inefficient private monopolies dominating the economy as a whole than they gain from their handful of shares. Thus there are those who perceive themselves to be better off as a result of Thatcherism, but who may well not be, not least for the reasons given in the first part of this section. In this category come those who may increasingly see the NHS as not for them for wholly ideological reasons.

It would be impossible for capitalism in the economy and commercialism in health care to be justified wholly by reference to the justifying ideology of individualism and equality of opportunity, as well as wealth production. While in its early days capitalism represented these values against a backdrop of a feudal society, it has long become clear that it requires subordination and control, especially of workers. Hence, pre-capitalist legitimations are necessary: the interests of the state and various atavistic impulses are part of the popular culture in Britain. The irony for free-marketeers is that the NHS is part of that legitimation in a conservative manner, as also in a radical manner.

The NHS is part of 'Great Britain's way' of providing a cheap, often hierarchical, health-care system – in part a noble socialist enterprise, but in part a legitimizing institution. It has survived a decade and more of Thatcherism, and the challenge now is to ensure it develops and fulfils its potential. It should not be an inegalitarian island, but a practical demonstration of how flexible socialism can be, both humane and efficient. The NHS has suffered in the 1980s from solutions to problems which only existed at the behest of their creators. Morale suffered, and, significantly, foreign commentators assumed the NHS model was now unhealthy or unstable. It was no longer the international jewel in the health-care crown, supplanted in that rôle by Canada. But nothing fundamental had changed, save relative underfunding, hostile rhetoric, and repeated reorganization employing business rhetoric, which NHS managers gobbled up from evangelical business bibles like children at the leftovers from an adult's feast. The time for posing is over. Good management, without jargon, is essential.

HOW IMPORTANT ARE HEALTH-CARE SYSTEMS?

It is important to remember that health care is only one of the influences upon the state of health of the population. Health status depends on many factors, among them genetic and natural factors. Social factors and environmental factors are also important: differences in health status between different social classes can be affected by the economic and political structure of society. Environmental conditions affect health. Poor housing affects health. The list, and indeed the list of theoretical categories, goes on.

One can draw a parallel between health and education in terms of how wider social factors affect both. There is a debate in educational policy circles as to the extent to which schools, as opposed to society and home background, affect a pupil's prospect of success. Pupils from a low social class, for example, may be able to be helped in school, but from a much more basic starting point. Thus, although school as an intervention may be effective, it may not be effective in taking pupils to the required standard for competition on equal terms for jobs and academic success with pupils from other social classes. In health care too, the health care system may only be icing on the cake as regards the production of health and health status. The health care system is likely to be helpful, but may only be an adjunct to other social conditions. The finishing line one reaches depends on where one starts, and how quickly one can move from a certain starting point.

It is therefore important, when addressing the health of the nation, to start off with objectives for health status, and improvements in health status for the population and for groups within the population. That is what public health is all about. Tracing the factors which prevent ill-health and prevent the full realization of positive health is important. An over-arching criticism of the 1989 White Paper is that it did not set objectives for health status for the population or for groups within it; it did not address the natural, personal, social, and environmental causes of ill-health and impediments to good health; and it betrayed a mechanistic obsession with managerial mechanics and untried ideologies in focusing upon the more economical use of limited resources employed in producing outputs of health care (operations; patients treated; and the usual gamut of potential parliamentary statistics).

It is an easy criticism to make, but a fundamentally true one, that the option of seeking priorities to improve the health status of the nation, and in particular, to instil a dose of equity therein, was ignored by the White Paper.

The thorny question of priorities: ethics and politics

Future priorities in health care are very difficult to define. There are many competing demands for scarce resources. Additional to this consideration is the fact that competing political and ethical approaches have varying implications for the use of resources in health care. It is often assumed that ethical concerns apply only at the level of the individual patient, yet choices are even more complicated than this.

It is in the realm of total public expenditure that the ultimately determining ethical and political choices arise. Let us take an extreme hypothetical example. A particular decision-maker is both a Roman Catholic who opposes abortion absolutely; opposes capital punishment; and believes it is society's moral obligation to provide resources to save all sick people who can technically be saved through the health-care system. In the short term he discovers that all these values cannot be fulfilled and is therefore faced with the hard choice of which value or values to downplay. This is not to behave immorally, but to behave as morally as possible, in other words to reconcile one's mix of values according to one's overall scheme of values. The decision-maker decides that although he is opposed to the death penalty and to abortion, since he is also opposed to the loss of life through lack of resources for health care, the sensible ethical choice is to save healthy and worthy people rather than to spend resources on preserving the lives of convicted murderers, or, for example, severely damaged foetuses.

Arguing that resources should be adequate may be a moral cop-out in the short term. That is why some philosophers opposed to technocratic systems of rationing in health care, such as the QALY (a construct which uses social preferences to assemble measures of quality of life resulting from medical procedures, in order to help assemble priorities for using limited money) are forced to advocate the pure lottery as a means of hard choice of last resort. If it is unethical to choose life for a healthy baby rather than a senile old man, and resources do not allow both, how else can a decision be made? It still requires ethical judgement as to, for example, whether to prefer to increase the quality of a life dramatically or actively to save the life of someone who will not live long. What is more, the QALY has been developed by economists whose ethical perspectives tend to be heavily loaded towards utilitarianism. So, in the end, the QALY rephrases questions rather than answering them.

Such stark choices rarely arise directly, although the smaller the population with which one is dealing – for example, a small island with a small health and general government budget – the more current such a choice may seem. Nevertheless, the overall system of government expenditure and allocation of resources to different sectors – for example, to the Department of Health, the Home Office, and to local government services – can determine the pattern of resources within which individual choices have to be made. Therefore, although no policy-maker will be playing God in deciding who shall live and who shall die, the overall system may constrain and guide exactly such choices. Furthermore, such value judgements will be necessary if the system of distribution of resources between Ministries is not to be purely political or *ad hoc*, in the most disreputable sense of these terms.

Society must therefore decide upon its values in allocating resources to different Ministries, for the reason that these Ministries will be carrying out different policies in order to fulfil different priorities. Within Ministries, how resources are allocated will determine, for example, whether funds are more likely to be available for kidney transplants for the aged, for community care for the aged, for genetic research to prevent defects at birth, and for all the other priorities. Individual ethical decisions will be constrained and directed by macro-ethical decisions. This applies generally in ethics: individual conduct towards our fellow citizens, for example, notions of reciprocal fairness, may be constrained and directed by the overall social and political structure within which we live, which is itself a focus for ethical concern.

Choosing a system of resource allocation in health care involves ethical considerations as well as methodological and technical considerations. Ethics is not merely to be left to the realm of individual decision-making. In allocating resources between regions, one may decide that population is the most important criterion. This has to be weighted in practice to account for the differing demands upon health-care systems made by different populations, for example, by the aged. After this, it may be thought sensible to weight the allocation of resources according to how much illness or death there is in a community. But there are different ways of doing this. Using death rates, even when these are standardized for age and sex, may emphasize the provision of resources to care for those conditions which are causing people to die. While this is legitimate, it is bound to favour the elderly population, not because death rates are not standardized for age, but because using death rates *per se* emphasizes conditions likely to strike in later life. Then the question arises, should resources be used for the purpose for which they were implicitly allocated?

This is a wholly separate debate from whether death rates are a significant correlate of illness generally, i.e. whether mortality measures morbidity adequately or not. Instead, the debate is geared to who receives the health care that these resources provide, on the assumption that resources are translated into plans for specific services. An alternative measure to standardized death rates is 'years of potential life lost'. This gives more emphasis to those conditions which strike the young, for example, motor accidents. Motor accidents may not be very significant on a scale of causes of death derived from standardized death rates, but leap in significance by the alternative measure of years of potential life lost, which attempts to gauge how many years of an individual's life is lost as a result of that death.

Another problem arises: is the health-care system the best medium in which to develop policies and apply resources to avert the loss of life years and improve health more generally? Even when thinking about the allocation of resources for health, one is drawn back to more general considerations on how to spend money to save life; possibly allocating the money to the Ministry of Transport might be more effective in this case.

It is impossible to apply a merely technical rationality to making such value judgements in allocating resources both within and between Ministries. Some basic ethical controversies arise in the debate between utilitarianism and formalist ethical theories. The latter is concerned with retributive or distributive justice, as opposed to the former's concern with maximization of benefit. For example, in choosing whether to spend money to keep alive a convicted murderer aged 80 or a 'healthy and worthy' child aged 15, one's ethical principles are going to be central. At one extreme there would be no contest. Any conception of utility – even measured in the broadest sense to include notions of worth to society – would make the choice an easy one. However, if one believes that all human life is of equal value, that the sense of living is the fundamental criterion of the worth of life, and that man cannot play God in making choices, there is no basis for allocating resources unless by the criterion of lottery. Some might object that this avoids rather than reaffirms a moral choice or moral stands. Nevertheless, the dilemma is clear.

If one avoids utilitarianism altogether, then systems for allocating resources to health care at the government level as well as individual choices at the hospital and unit level will be very difficult. If there is a moral necessity to treat all equally on the basis of their being living human beings, then notions such as the QALY become useless; they have already been demonstrated to lead to bizarre choices in any case. However, by a less austere moral theory, QALYs may have a rôle to play at the margin of decision-making. The import of utilitarian-style measures such as the QALY is to argue that resources ought to be distributed on the basis of a formula which rewards effective health care to those who can by some subjective criterion benefit most in longevity and quality of life. However, it also depends upon a value judgement as to how to compare in one equation the preservation of life and the amelioration of life.

Using the QALY therefore would imply evaluating the need to alleviate and prevent illness and promote health among the youngest and the most deserving. This leads us to the question of the slippery slope: is it true that it is only a quantitative and not a qualitative leap from such an approach to the approach of, say, the Nazis? On one interpretation, this is evidently not the case. Doctors, health service managers, and politicians make such choices every day. Surely it is better to make such choices by open and attemptedly rational, however imperfect, criteria rather than by merely *ad hoc* criteria? On another interpretation, however, it is better to avoid such choices altogether and to fund health services as adequately as possible without drawing such distinctions.

The problem for this optimistic view is that some criterion will have to be adopted. If one says the government ought not to be involved in making such choices, one is merely leaving it to the private marketplace – whether of money or of ideas or of choices – to do one's dirty work.

Arguing that it is only public choices involving public expenditure which confront such dilemmas is evading the issue. By a number of political criteria, especially socialist ones, public duty involves financing needs publicly and ensuring that society is not denying meaningful choice to those without private wealth for private consumption of health care.

For example, one may be able to increase the total quantity of health care available and the total preservation of life by moving resources into the public domain. This itself involves an ethical stance, and arguing against it that what people do with their own money is their business, is only acceptable under individualist, market-based, ethical principles. Such principles, especially combined with limited government expenditure, imply that resources will not be available to provide certain things for the needy, whereas these things can be purchased privately. Is a need a right? Is health care a right? If so, how can private care be justified if public care has to deny certain needs? Only in a land of plenty will the private sector wither due to satisfaction with the public sector.

No society is going to allocate all resources to all Ministries on the basis of cold or rational criteria. Such criteria may not involve a slippery slope, but they are never going to replace politics in any case. Real slippery slopes must, however, be avoided. For example, one might reach the extreme position that in order to allocate resources to preserve life, capital punishment for various crimes should be supported even by those who in principle oppose it in order to ensure that the money saved from caring for offenders is used to expand the quantum of health care available. This is patently unacceptable, indeed absurd, to most people. However, when one attempts to argue from first principles that this is so, it is not easy to find consensus. In practice, preservation of life through health and social care will have to be combined with the existence of basic universal human rights.

It is when trying to observe this dictum within health care, as well as when arguing for a spread of resources between health care and other realms, that difficulties arise. One sees, for example, the controversy between enthusiastic believers in the QALY approach and those who believe that other conceptions of human rights must take priority.

A worthwhile challenge exists, however difficult. Society must produce adequate political and ethical consensus upon social goals to inform allocation of resources both to the health-care sector and other sectors. Formulae for the allocation of these resources over a country within health and other sectors ought to be compatible with the ethical principles which inform approaches to the preservation of life. In consequence, there will be more hope that society's ethical values will be realized or approximated in making the individual decisions when working within these resources. Planning for outcomes is unlikely to be compatible with unplanned markets, or markets planned and managed purely out of pragmatism.

Incorporating choice without weakening the NHS

If consumerism demanded, it would be possible to devise a system whereby residents within a health authority could choose either to remain with the NHS as they had known it by referral by GPs freely when required, or to join an HMO-style organization which offered them guaranteed, contracted benefits for the price of less freedom in referral. These experiments could develop naturally, in line with both patient/consumer/citizen preference, and the capacity of health authorities to create within their management HMO-style units. This would, like the White Paper's consequences, probably require merged, larger district health authorities.

Such HMO management units would employ GPs, and contract with providers such as hospitals. Thus, if they took off, hospitals would have to compete to sell services to them in order to recoup revenue lost as a result of financing the HMOs by capitation for those willing to join.

In the longer term, patients could join HMOs competing on a non-geographical basis: HMOs of good repute could recruit outside district boundaries. Thus, a competitive structure could exist alongside a traditional NHS, but only if enough patients were interested to make it a viable reform, with catchment population for each HMO of at least 50,000 to prevent fiscal problems, through atypically heavy case-load and usage due to the population being inadequately balanced.

This is but an idea, if competition is inevitable. But a marketplace in consumption, created, for example, by giving each consumer a voucher, does not solve the problem of ensuring that need, not just demand, is addressed, which is a social and sociological problem and not one susceptible to a mechanistic market solution. Another type of reform could be implemented without sacrificing the right of patients and doctors to make choices. The paternalism of the doctor would not have to be replaced by the paternalism of the manager, as happens in the White Paper's agenda.

An alternative to the district as the rationing agent in Britain could be the amendment of existing financial and institutional mechanism to provide for central reimbursement of health-care costs on an individual basis for agreed treatments at agreed rates. Such an amendment of the regional and district system, either pre- or post-White Paper, would not put an end to planning, although it would be altered in nature, since projections of need and demand in different areas would have to be made. However, the pretence of the White Paper – that district-based competition can still fulfil populations' needs equitable – would no longer be necessary.

Planning to meet need, yet observing cost requirements and limiting inefficiency, could allow regions to indulge in strategic planning and then to reimburse, prospectively, providing institutions. Clearly, some new arrangements would be necessary. Competition's textbook benefits would be achieved by a regulatory and planning rôle rather than by an unrealistic and mechanistic rigmarole of cut-throat yet duplicative action by districts and units.

It would, however, resemble the introduction of a public insurance system, or rather, since the third party element which creates a problematic dissolution of immediate financial responsibility in insurance schemes would be absent, a public reimbursement system, with patient rights nationally based. It could be compatible with a stronger rôle for individual hospitals managed as units, which would allow decentralized management and responsibility.

Greater central control of which technologies were allowable, and which were not, would be a possible benefit. Less flexibility, and indeed less overall planning in certain areas, e.g. in regional or district decisions as to resource allocation and planning, and more in others, e.g. in the design of incentives to control individual costs and regulate individual specialties or facilities, occasioned by an individual reimbursement system, would be another consequence.

DRGs could be used to reimburse providing institutions in accord with prospective planning and reimbursement. DRGs are a system for grouping clinical conditions, finding their reasonable costs and reimbursing accordingly. A consequence of such a system – providing a guarantee that care would be available as long as the treatment was advisable to the more centrally determined list of agreed NHS procedures, could well be much greater spending on the NHS. The myth that we have at present a free-at-the-point-of-use and freely available service for all reasonable illnesses and needs could no longer so easily co-exist with widely discrepant rationing of care.

Such rationing would become more visible, even though the ability to put things right would not easily be forthcoming. This is because the supply side in health care, even were money more available on the demand side, would be only partly capable of responding. The mobility of medical manpower is not necessarily great, and travel to care might have to grow. That is, a different financing system, plus guarantees of care, is a theoretical option which might face bottlenecks in practice.

Failings and omissions would admittedly be more in the public eye: inability to secure treatment when treatment was supposedly available would be more of a national issue, and would be likely to attract wider, possibly national, public perception. The system would then be working for patients, with the benefits of good incentives which related providers' remuneration to workload and improved access and equity.

Again, however, the system would require more resources to work well, as do most reform proposals. The above proposal has some analogies with Canadian health care, which has supplanted Britain's as the shining example? This is probably because Britain's financial difficulties, and the government's equivocal attitude to the NHS in the

1980s, have tarnished the NHS abroad. The NHS model was always feared by American right-wingers, but until recently was admired by liberal commentators around the world.

It is still the best system. Improvements in efficiency and in mode of provision are compatible with more generous financing: both policies should be pursued. After all, even when hospitals are rewarded according to their workload, there may not be enough money so that all referred patients can be paid for by purchasers. Then rationing by some means is inevitable.

In the US, attempts to control costs by insurance companies have led to strict resource management, for example, in Johns Hopkins Hospital, within clinical regimes which make British medical audit in a context of resource awareness a teddy-bears' picnic by comparison.

The question for Britain is: can we do what rationing is regrettably necessary without institutionalizing rationing? QALYs necessitate choices between specialties: do we do hips or hearts? It is better to allow doctors to manage within their specialty, and to ensure that no rationing system is too rigid by threatening whole specialties. Only then will doctors in specialties share with overall managers of hospitals and health authorities the task of humane resource management.

Chapter Seven

The central changes to the NHS: 1991 and after

There was considerable attention given from late in 1990 to the middle of 1991 to the alleged slowing of NHS reform, a trend set in motion by the replacement of first Mr Clarke with Mr Waldegrave at the Department of Health, then Mrs Thatcher with Mr Major in 10 Downing Street.

There are trends identified with the White Paper, *Working for Patients*, however, which point to a sea-change in attitudes to the NHS by policy-makers and managers. Firstly, the logic of the Paper calls for explicit rationing of care according to priorities by purchasers, to replace implicit or tacit rationing by providers after a process of free referral. In early 1991, the chief executive of the NHS management executive, instructed regional health authorities to set conditions for access to waiting-lists. However minor these may be in practice for political reasons, an important precedent has been set in implementing the White Paper's philosophy. Later in 1991, waiting-lists were cut by removing from them cases for which contracts were not to be placed by purchasing districts. Although, in practice, doctors in hospitals still make waiting-lists from those patients referred, whether within or without a contract from a purchaser, waiting-lists should in theory now be the responsibility of the purchaser.

Secondly, the language of consumer choice is increasingly deployed, but in inverse proportion to the possibilities for choice by consumers and patients, after the implementation of the White Paper in 1991, following the NHS and Community Care Act. This also shadows the White Paper's stress upon working for patients in its rhetoric, yet upon making the manager, rather than the patient's advocate, the doctor, responsible for translating needs and priorities into contracts with providers.

Yet a basic fact remains: in Britain, consumers cannot choose their purchasers. Contracts by purchasers with providers reflect the need for economy as a first priority. It is in the gradual abandonment of a radical market strategy, internal or otherwise, that undoubtedly the brakes have been applied. But the use of the White Paper as a tool for managers to enforce economy and reorientate employee relations throughout the

NHS, just as the competitive tendering process instigated in 1983 did in a limited sphere, is increasingly developed.

The purchaser–provider separation is a myth, except where NHS trusts are the providers. Even there, Mr Waldegrave has recently announced significant restrictions on trust freedom to pay market rates and invest via capital markets. For purchasers (districts) in fact employ and train the key workforce, doctors, employed by providers. In practice, closely linked providing and purchasing management teams will be an expanded bureaucratic force against which other voices have less of a hearing. So, less change than expected in one direction, but more in another. Only if, in future, trusts were to dominate the supply side of care and GP fund holders were to dominate the demand side, would a more convincing market exist.

Markets require competition to provide efficiency. If unnecessary investments, failures and closures are not permitted, there will be no competitive market. That is no bad thing. So why not admit that strategic planning is not a discredited adjunct of pre-1990 Eastern Europe, but the essential tool of the modern general management of the NHS? Then we could allow service provision to reflect agreement between doctors, managers and patients' advocates, within allowed budgets.

In the end we are left with the contracting process, and the purchaser's ability to identify need, yet the rhetoric of consumerism. This may produce two forces for higher spending. Firstly, rationing based on purchasers' priorities translated through into contracts with providers may still be politically unacceptable, hence, the Interleukin case at the Christie Hospital, Manchester. Secondly, consumers will demand production-line medicine and trendy procedures, whether they meet expert-defined need or not. In aggregate, these forces will push for higher NHS spending.

This may be fine. After all, we are a very low spender on health in Britain, and public spending is the most effective and efficient way to increase expenditure – on health. The problem hitherto has been the conventional wisdom, on right and left, that only moving to an insurance-based or partly private financing system could boost aggregate spending.

It would be an irony to be savoured if the long-term fallout of the Review were higher public spending and little or no reliance on competitive markets. The Chancellor's statement on 6 November 1991 suggested more money for the NHS was to buy off unpopularity – an irony, given the origins of the Review.

THE NHS AND ELECTORAL POLITICS

The NHS Review was instituted early in 1988 in an attempt by the government to divert a debate about alleged underfunding of the NHS to a debate about efficiency in the provision of health care. More than three years later, the debate about underfunding of the NHS resurfaced in even more virulent form. It seemed that the government of Mr John Major was on the defensive, both about alleged under-spending on the NHS and about what the media and public perceived as damaging consequences arising from the implementation of the NHS Act embracing the White Paper *Working for Patients*. The Vale of Glamorgan and Monmouth bye-elections did not exactly suggest to the Conservatives that they were trusted on health.

Increased public awareness of overt rationing in health care, as purchasing health authorities decide what can and cannot be provided on the NHS, was joined by a strong public perception that certain of the changes to the NHS involved unfairness. There was much publicity about significant job losses at hospitals, which were part of the first wave of self-governing trusts. These may or may not be related to the policy intentions behind the White Paper. Some cuts would have happened anyway, but trusts were rightly seen as a fragmenting force in the provision of care, leading to a US–style duplication of both medical equipment and information technology.

More central to the philosophy of the White Paper was the ability of GP practices holding their own budgets to negotiate contracts with hospitals which involve their patients having shorter waiting times than patients whose care is contracted for by a purchasing health authority. It was this factor which has allowed the Labour Party successfully to attack the government for promoting inequity in access to health care. Emotive phrases such as 'queue jumping' can, it seems, be given some substance. There are two levels at which this policy can be analysed. Firstly, one can look at the economic logic lying behind the new arrangements. Secondly, one can look at the likely political consequences.

THE ECONOMIC LOGIC

It is important to examine the reality of the incentives created by allowing two purchasers – district health authorities and GPs holding their own budgets – to contract with providing hospitals and other suppliers of health care. It might be thought that having two purchasers rather than one would fragment the purchasers' bargaining power *vis-à-vis* the provider, and increase the relative power of the provider in any contract negotiations. To some extent this is true. After all, recent media headlines emphasize how hospitals are exploiting their negotiations with GPs in effect to tell health authority purchasers that they are second best; that their referred patients must take second place in the queue behind fund-holding GPs' patients. The argument presumably is that the latter have a smaller number of patients and a flexibility to refer elsewhere. Certainly, in the US, a multiplicity of purchasers gives power to providers, even when providers are operating at significantly less than full capacity and when supply may exceed demand in the aggregate. This is only part of the story; for the aggregate money available to purchasers of health care in the US is huge in both absolute and relative terms.

In Britain, although latent demand certainly exceeds supply in health care, actual demand expressed by NHS purchasers is severely limited by the amount of money available to a strictly cash-limited NHS. In consequence, there is a limit to the manipulation of the purchaser by the provider. The British hospital/provider has to put together a coalition of purchasers, if any sort of market at all is working, in order to attract the required business and break-even.

As in the US, the relative power of providers and purchasers is determined by two factors: the relative ability to exploit both a monopoly position of their own, and a competitive position of their opponent on the one hand; and the relative quantum of supply and demand in aggregate on the other. In Britain the hospital may have some bargaining advantage where it can divide and rule among more than one purchaser, but also the relative disadvantage that it relies on all or most of the purchasers in order to put together a viable business plan. In other words, fragmented purchasers are complementary, not competing; there was no 'competition' alternative in Britain to the previous purchasing monopoly. In fact, larger consortia of purchasers, including GPs, were developing in 1991, to cope with the power of monopoly providers. Hardly a marketplace.

One consequence of this, relevant to the current political debate, is that the power of GP purchasers may be overrated. Health authority purchasers account for significantly more funds, even in areas where GP purchasing is salient. There is nothing to stop a health authority purchaser from threatening to remove business from providers who give preference to GP purchasers. Health authority purchasers often rely on their local providers, or have an interest in keeping their local providers in business. But this cuts both ways. It is true that a health authority will not be able to remove all its patients lock, stock, and barrel, to another provider, but there is nothing to stop it threatening to make contracts elsewhere to a financial total equivalent to the business being offered by the GPs in return for their patients jumping the queue or receiving other forms of preferential treatment. It is simply a matter of the purchasers seeking to outdo each other in bargaining *vis-à-vis* the provider. This gives the provider some choice, but not unlimited choice where both purchasers must at the end of the day be pleased in some respect. In other words, there is not excess actual demand.

How such theory works out in practice is naturally of political significance. What we have is a series of economic and bargaining incentives which may or may not work out to the advantage of individual patients, or indeed of all patients, through a better or more efficient health service. Different scenarios can be traced, and in so doing the bureaucratic costs of operating such a market must not be discounted.

THE POLITICAL CONSEQUENCES

Perhaps more significant is the likely political consequence of operating such a policy. It is significant that Mr Major, in reply to Mr Kinnock in 'Prime Minister's Question Time' (Tuesday, 7 May and Thursday 9 May 1991), did not seek to defend the new arrangements by arguing for their beneficial effect, presumably in the long run. Instead, he sought in effect to play down the notion that any radical change in practice would occur as a result of GP fundholding. That is, in line with the safety-first policy following the departure of Mrs Thatcher, one way led to believe that the White Paper would not really change all that much. This argument was surely a political loser for the government. If all the anxiety, and in some cases tangible fear, of inequity were occurring for little purpose and at much bureaucratic and propaganda costs, the government surely stood condemned on the grounds of fatuousness.

In politics generally in Britain in the early 1990s there was a public mood for safety first, and for both consolidation and greater equity in public life following the turmoil of the Thatcher years, especially the latter years when the raft of policy initiatives was increasingly out of tune with the public mood. Mr Major therefore would have run the serious risk of pleasing the think-tanks of the radical right yet losing the election. Such a strategy seemed unlikely. What we were therefore left with was the phenomenon of a government moving ahead, on paper, with a series of unpopular reforms, which by the government's own admission and indeed, design (post-Thatcher), would not make a tremendous amount of difference to health care in the country, save to make it more bureaucratic. This is especially ironical given that the reforms were allegedly market driven.

The Labour Party was until recently on the defensive concerning the policy debate in health care since the White Paper was announced. This did not stop it from still being the party most people trusted with the health service. It has not in fact needed to be particularly innovative in its thinking concerning the NHS, although recent proposals from the Labour Party have shown a willingness to think in terms of how the benefits of both planning and yet also sharper economic incentives in the provision of health care can be combined.

It is silly to alarm the public and mess around with the provision of health care if there are not substantial and even radical policies being pursued to improve its provision. If we really wanted to move to a system whereby consumers chose their GPs just as people choose HMOs in the US, on the grounds of their ability to deliver good health care at a reasonable price, then GP fundholding on the demand side, and opted-out hospitals on the supply side, might be a good idea. In a British context, however, we have probably come full circle in that such ideas are gradually returning to the right wing think-tanks whence they came in the first place. The problem is that the Conservative government adopted such ideas partially, and was stuck with them.

THE FUTURE

One beneficial aspect of the NHS reforms was, in theory, the ability of the purchasing health authority to determine priorities on behalf of its population, and then to achieve these in the most effective and efficient manner possible, through negotiation with providers, whether these providers are its own hospitals or not. Yet many of the scandals highlighted by the media in 1991 concerned opted-out hospitals offering packages of care to purchasing authorities at higher prices in return for prompt treatment, for example Alder Hey Hospital in Liverpool.

Concern over such a phenomenon is justified. There is evidence that short-termism and financial opportunism will affect both providers and purchasers and distort health-care priorities. In the absence of adequate cost information, it is impossible to regulate such a state of affairs (as Mr Waldegrave promised to do in the House of Commons on 9 May 1991). Given lack of certainty about costs, it is impossible to know whether hospitals are making unjustified profits or presenting unfair bills to the purchaser.

Moreover, the division of hospitals into self-governing trusts and directly managed hospitals still under the direct control of health authorities, which are now schizophrenic in both purchasing and providing, does not help. For trusts are freer to decide their mix of activities and range of prices than directly managed hospitals. This distorts competition, and promotes inequity. For example, the Liverpool University Trusts received adverse publicity in September 1991 for a draft business plan drawn up by management consultants which stressed financial opportunities at the cost of ignoring certain patient groups. To prevent this, the government had to step in, to promise continuing direct accountability of trusts to the Department of Health. Devolution and markets?

District health authorities have a responsibility to make decisions on behalf of their citizens concerning the mix of health-care activities to be offered within limited budgets. This means that inevitably some districts will have different priorities from other districts. Thus, someone living in Devon may have less chance of a cataract operation than someone in Manchester, for deliberate as well as accidental reasons based, for example, on inefficiency.

In the pre-reform NHS, waiting-lists and times varied widely across the country. Ironically, many of the more optimistic commentators saw in the reforms a chance to tackle this. GPs, for example, would have information on where waiting-lists were shorter so they could refer patients in that direction, if they were willing to travel. It was only a short step from this to giving the GPs their own budgets. The effect on equity was not really discussed at that stage of the reasoning. And it is a perfectly fair point that to improve the overall performance of the service may lead to a disturbance in equity in the sense of equal misery. But in practice, GPs without their own budgets are frequently prevented from referring to providers where waiting-lists are shorter because districts have chosen for financial reasons not to make contracts with these providers.

The challenge faced by those forming an alternative to the White Paper policy is to diminish dogmatic adherence to market ideology and its concomitant denigration of the NHS's great international advantage: capacity for effective planning. Health authorities ought to assess need and then ensure that their providers are attuned to meeting that need through a planning system which offers effective incentives. A courageous policy of this sort is just as likely to meet with conservative opposition as the present Government's policy. Labour's policy documents in 1990 and 1991 represented only the beginning of a strategy.

In conclusion, a coherent policy for a successful NHS should include:

- Adherence to the principle that money follows the patient, but in a manner beneficial to the patient. The present government's White Paper has this policy allegedly as its cornerstone, but neglects to mention that a patient's referral has to be sanctioned through a contract before any monetary provision is made for it, let alone that money following the patient. In consequence, the pre-White-Paper NHS allowed greater freedom of referral of the patient, although in the absence of adequate finance, queues at the doors of providers often resulted. One of the confusions of the post-White-Paper NHS is that only where patients are registered with fundholding GPs can they have at least the possibility of a real freedom of referral plus money following the patients but even then only for certain limited categories of care (primarily diagnostic services and elective surgery).
- Consistency in types of contracts placed with providers by GPs who hold their own budgets (if this clause is retained in the future) and purchasing health authorities. This will allow the latter to have as

much bargaining power as GPs. Currently, purchasing health authorities are obliged to place block-and-cost-per-volume contracts simply to guarantee the availability of services and an expected volume respectively. The consequence of this is that they have less bargaining power to remove contracts, in order for example to try to match the bargaining power of GPs who can act more flexibly. As stated above, the relative scarcity of finance in the NHS allows purchasers to have bargaining power *vis-à-vis* providers, even where there is a fragmentation in purchasing. It is important, however, that this bargaining power does not work to the detriment of equity in that patients dependent on different purchasers have different conditions for access. Block contracts are of little use in promoting the White Paper's primary objective, 'relating income to workloads'. For workload is variable, just as pre-White Paper. Hence, financial crises continue.

- The idea of a Citizens' Charter may be a good one. The basic decision has, however, to be taken as to whether the citizen is a consumer, for example, shopping around for different types of purchaser as the luckier type of US citizen can shop around for HMOs, or as Dutch citizens, in their new system, can shop around for different types of sickness fund or insurance company, or whether the citizen exercises his/her rights through more collective means. The latter might include guaranteed standards of service, including access to preventive health and health-related social services, where national priorities have identified these. The present government is allegedly devising a programme of health targets based upon recognition of the many social causes of health and ill-health. For these to be meaningful, access to health must not be dependent upon geographical or chance political factors throughout the country.

  What is clear is that the Patients Charter of 1991 is a superficial initiative, and an example of centralist regulation which is opposed to the philosophy of the White Paper.

- A planning system which reconciles incentives for providers to attract business with national priorities based upon equity and effectiveness. Instead of a market-based contracting system, whether fully operative or merely symbolic, a revitalized planning system can avoid the pitfalls of both opting-out and fragmentation and confusion in purchasing. Yet it can, with a will, be flexible enough to avoid the bureaucracy and centralism which has undermined planning in the past, along with planning's subversion to political fads and political bargaining. In other words, planning can co-exist with decentralized responsibility in an operational sense to providers.

In more ideological terms, a sensible policy for health care will recognize that the health service is a public service, where citizens are not merely economic consumers; that nevertheless economic incentives can be beneficial to providers; and that merely replacing the alleged centralism of planning with the centralism of a government-dictated marketplace is futile.

INTERPRETING HEALTH POLICY

Let us consider what appear to be two similar policies based on different intentions. The Conservative Party tends nowadays to argue that, while the NHS is to be preserved, value for money from the existing budget must be achieved and that vast new sums cannot be expected to increase spending on the health service. In consequence, tighter control of the medical profession and tighter enforcement of national priorities through contracting for the provision of health care are to be promulgated. At first this can easily be dismissed as cutting spending on social programmes, consistent with a policy of lowering government expenditure in order to lower taxes and stimulate both private investment in the economy and the traditional capitalist inegalitarianism. Another interpretation, however, seems not very dissimilar to what the Labour government was in effect attempting, and failing to achieve, in the 1970s. Then, the power of the medical profession was hailed to be too great, and it was thought necessary to seek new priorities in health spending. The mechanism for achieving these was not clear and priorities such as the Cinderella Services were not achieved to any great extent in practice.

It can be argued of course that the earlier Labour government was not seeking such a policy in the context of hostility to the NHS. Objectively, however, rates of growth in spending on the NHS have been similar, especially when put in an international context, under both Labour governments in the 1970s and Conservative governments in the 1980s and early 1990s. The question, therefore, arises: whatever the rhetoric, whatever the real intention, were the policies the same?

Some have even argued that the Labour government's policy was even more inegalitarian in that, while it was objectively similar to later Conservative policy, it was conducted in an atmosphere hostile to economic growth and economic opportunity, and that therefore the overall wealth of society was decreased, decreasing in turn the amount of money available for the health service given as static percentage of the GDP available for the health service. In consequence, an egalitarian institution was susceptible to less growth. In the author's view, this is not true, but the point is clear: do intentions matter at all, or is it only objective outcome which matters?

Intentions do matter. After all, a Conservative government's argument that it is betraying its own natural supporters by being harsh on the doctors can easily be countered by pointing out that the hidden agenda of such policy, which may be occurring in practice, is to encourage doctors who do wish to be part of the capitalist class to increase practice in the private sector. It can then be argued that Labour's earlier policy of driving private practice out of NHS hospitals in fact increases the private sector quite dramatically. The point nevertheless is that, although Conservative policy may have been geared to getting better value for money, within the NHS, its overall effect (an acceptable consequence if not overt intention among all Conservative policy makers) has been to boost the private sector in a continuing and structural manner as opposed to Labour's unintended result of driving existing private practice out of NHS hospitals.

More importantly, one can consider the effect of different policies upon staff in the organization. The pro-private tendency in Conservative policy, while not measured easily in terms of percentages of GNP falling upon public health care and the like, may have convinced NHS staff that they were working for a second-class institution.

One can therefore argue that different intentions produce different results, not through dry statistics taken as a snapshot at one point in time, but through the effect upon behaviour. It is important to conduct research into the effect upon staff of the communication of policy, as such an effect can have a long-term influence upon the implementation of medium and long-term policy objectives. To continue the above example: Labour policy in the 1970s, never implemented, had aspirations towards tighter control of the medical profession and greater regulation of health service priorities. Conservative policy can be interpreted likewise, through the system of contracting after the White Paper of 1989. However, the policies are rather different when viewed as to longer-term effects: the Labour policy would have created different NHS priorities within a total system of greater emphasis upon social policy and the social wage. Conservative policy, however, would have implemented more stringent control in an environment of diminishing staff morale within the NHS and diminishing consumer belief in the NHS as a valuable provider in the marketplace based upon increasing consumer affluence. In other words, Labour policy would have been conceivably socialist; Conservative policy would have squeezed value for money out of a welfare wedge.

In consequence, Conservative policy can be seen to be more like US health policy in one important respect: doctors working for public services would have been working in worse conditions than doctors working in private services. This would reinforce the argument that Conservatives are not after all being inconsistent in grading down NHS doctors: they would in fact be providing an outlet for such doctors to join the capitalist class through greater private work or through greater reimbursement in less regulated quasi-private hospitals, i.e. NHS trusts, which had opted-out and which could pay doctors large amounts of money for bringing their formerly private work to the hospital.

US politics works by harnessing the private market on the one hand and government intervention on behalf of favoured interest groups on the other hand. In consequence, attacks on the medical profession through tighter reimbursements occur within a context of historically great power held by the medical profession. It is nevertheless the case that doctors dissatisfied with tight regulation when working for programmes relying on government funding or when working for, for example, HMOs, are still relatively more privileged within society than doctors in Britain wholly engaged in public-sector work. Furthermore, they can seek greater benefit outside government programmes altogether. A combination of private-market opportunity and government subsidy of favoured interest groups in the US helps, on an extremely differential and inegalitarian basis, different interest groups and professions to prosper.

In Britain, the right wing in politics tends not to use such an amalgam of policy to benefit its favoured groups. It rather advocates private-sector opportunity from those who wish to be capitalists, without dramatic government subsidy except in the general business arena of the economy, and argues that professions working in the public sector must accept increasing control.

This admittedly reverses the earlier Conservative policy of being tolerant towards affluent professions working in the public sector. However, as spending on the welfare state is brought under control, this is not so much a freely chosen reversal of policy as a predictable trend. In consequence, the difference between what is here characterized as Conservative and Labour policy may be quite substantial when viewed as part of the greater whole. What is more, Conservative policy which may seem to be stealing Labour's clothes may be seen to be consistently conservative, and Labour policy, which may be interpreted by cynics as stealing Conservatives' clothes may be quite compatible with socialist doctrine.

THEORY AND PRACTICE REVIEWED

The central debate concerning the distribution of power in British health care naturally concerns who increasingly holds power. The widespread view in political science used to assert that the medical profession is dominant in influencing priorities, both in the making and implementing of health policy. This may always have been a simplification. However, it is now yielding to ɼ new orthodoxy: that general management acting at the behest of government is capable of reorienting priorities in the health care system by reference to an agenda substantially different to that of the medical profession. This has created some problems for analysts, especially the major trends in this direction which have occurred under 12 years of Conservative governments since 1979. After all, are the Conservatives not supposed to be the doctors' friends? Are not doctors part of the upper strata of society that one would expect a Conservative government to protect? This may be so in one sense. However, another agenda has preoccupied the Conservative administrations of this time.

This agenda has consisted in the achievement of better value for money in the public sector and strict limiting of available services through public means. In consequence, doctors eking out their career in the public sector cannot expect very favourable treatment. They are likely to find much lusher pastures if they increase their private-sector work. Early moves in the 1980s encouraged this, although later the clash between allowing doctors access to the private sector to remove grievance about public-sector conditions has been moderated in an attempt to ensure that it does not lead to less value for money through doctors' NHS contracts.

One can characterize Conservative policy throughout the economy as a whole as encouraging private-sector activity through lower rates of taxation and various special incentives. In health care particularly the focus has been upon extracting more product from limited resources. Although the early days of the Prime Minister's Review of the NHS in 1988 and the early debate following the publication of the White Paper *Working for Patients*, in 1989, stressed competition and increasing use of market forces, the end result seems to be that these are rather peripheral and that the name of the game is tighter monitoring of contracts to ensure that more is squeezed from a limited budget in terms of quantity of health care provided. This is not to deny that debates about quality, medical audit, and so forth, are recurring, but ought to be seen in the context of using a tendering not necessarily market process to achieve efficiency savings as occurred with the earlier competitive tendering episodes dating from 1983, at that time concerned only with ancillary services.

In consequence, two possible routes for the NHS are possible. The right-wing route involves strict limitations on public spending, which in turn encourages private insurance and the private sector, and therefore differentiates sharply between doctors' conditions when working for the NHS and when working for the private sector. Doctors would not be part of the capitalist class capable of benefiting from private sector activity. The other route involves the Labour party using tighter monitoring of health service activity, not in order to limit public sector activity to the status of a welfare wedge, but in order to ensure greater value for money, albeit in a context of fairness to employees, from a more stable and indeed better-funded public service.

This is a very simplistic picture of course. After all, the creation of self-governing trusts allow – in theory – private and public sector health care to be delivered under one roof. In consequence, what was formerly private-sector work may now be work for the trust, which will mean that the doctor is paid a unified, albeit much higher, salary to embrace what was formerly his/her private work. Thus, a growing separation between public and private work may not actually happen in the institutional sense. Nevertheless, Conservative stewardship, whether under Mr Major or whoever, is associated with something resembling the former scenario.

In terms of the power debate, it would be difficult to argue for pluralism in interpreting who wields power. Doctors and other health-care professions have less power both in the bargaining process and in their determining of policy; likewise, they have less influence at health authority and lower levels in determining the mix of activities and therefore health outcomes. Managers may be considered to be the new corporate rationalizers, but in a British context they do not have enough power independent of government to be called a new class. The government in Britain, in the 1980s and up to 1991, increasingly sought to centralize control, via placemen in health authorities, and also in management, to a lesser extent. The House of Commons Select Committee on Health was chaired in 1991 by Mr Nicholas Winterton, who deplored the lack of independence of NHS authority chairmanships, under the guise, it could be argued, of separating good management from Parliamentary politics.

In Britain the government is indeed the source of power. The question is in whose interests or on whose behalf is government operating? This begins to sound like a neo-Marxist interpretation of health policy being made in the interests of the economy as a whole, and therefore in the interests of the capitalist economy in Britain, but that would itself be an oversimplification. As already stated, there are alternative political contexts in which a tighter-managed, centrally controlled NHS could be interpreted.

What is clear is that there is a choice to be made as to whether we want a health service operated at the behest of a centralizing, right wing, government or at the behest of a social democratic government, representing the views of different groups. The latter view would tend to a pluralist interpretation, but not really in the sense of the pluralist literature, most of which derives from the US. For British pluralism of a centralized sort would not be fragmented and would therefore have the scope for encouraging more co-ordinated social programmes and more effective social reform. This is not to deny that US-style pluralism based on decentralized interest group activity is largely absent in Britain.

It is now probably the province of the left, which after 12 years of the Thatcherite state, is becoming suspicious of centralized activity altogether. This has historical irony, in that the left has traditionally been the party of centralizing authority.

It is interesting to note that on paper the British NHS shared characteristics with the former health systems of the former eastern European Communist countries. In other words, it is a centrally funded service which is allegedly centrally planned; where resources are allocated for a mixture of central and local purposes by a mixture of formulae and political decision; and where staffs's duties are by and large centrally ascribed. Naturally, there has been considerable change to these characteristics, or at least some of them, in Britain in the last two years, although considerably less than there has been and will continue to be in the former eastern European countries. Nevertheless, it is important to show, using terms such as pluralism why the reality was very different.

Britain has been a pluralist society in a broader sense of the term. In other words, the word pluralism may be used within Western democratic societies to characterize a degree of openness in the policy-making process, and receptivity to all, in some versions of pluralist theory, as opposed to merely possibility of social forces opposing government will through the democratic and governmental process. Britain is certainly a pluralist country in the latter sense; although others could argue that it is an élitist country in terms of the prospective outline at the beginning of this chapter.

In the former eastern European countries, however, there was no pluralism in implementing, yet alone making, health policy. Therefore, one can argue that although market mechanisms to bolster consumerism, on the one hand, and scientific management techniques to squeeze the maximum productivity out of the organization, on the other hand, were absent at an earlier stage in Britain, nevertheless, a brake was placed on the inefficiency of central governmental control by the pluralistic interaction in Britain of different professions and indeed different trade unions at health authority level. It is no secret that the Conservative governments of the 1980s have been trying to diminish this aspect of pluralism by instituting more unified top-down management and, for example, the removal of political influence on health authorities. This could be seen as a centralizing strategy. It is often claimed to be a decentralizing strategy, however, in that greater autonomy is given to management to promulgate efficiency oriented changes through scientific management and different management of human resources.

There are fundamentally two routes to mitigate the stifling bureaucracy of a centrally planned system. One is to open up to the market, as is happening in some eastern European countries, at least on paper; the other is to replace it with devolved management, but a diminution not an increase of political pluralism. In the former eastern European countries, there is a demand from below, i.e. from the people, for increased political pluralism in the implementation of policy as well as in the making of policy. This may not be occurring in practice, as for example in Hungary where the new centre-right governing party is behaving with some authoritarianism. However, the two routes may not be compatible: one can have pluralism or one can have streamlined management. And the market is yet another option, which may or may not be compatible with genuine political pluralism and popular participation; which may or may not be compatible with effective strategic management to meet health need.

Evidence from abroad suggests that a market in provision of care, and certainly private insurance in financing of care, retard rather than promote effective management by government and health authorities to meet need.

An epitaph for the White Paper, long after the Conservatives have modified it and Labour may later have modified it further, may well be: 'Planning was killed; long live planning, in a more flexible form'.

The Labour party was not opposed in 1991 to all of the elements of the White Paper. It certainly opposed opting-out by self-governing trusts, and sought to argue that they were almost opting-out of the NHS itself, not just of health authorities. The political heat surrounding the Monmouth by-election in May 1991 showed the government to be losing the popular argument, what is more. People were convinced that staff were no longer employed by the NHS or health authority, that land and the estate was somehow privatized and that social need and equity were no longer criteria in planning access to health care.

In the longer term, the life of the White Paper may be identified with the rise and fall of credulity concerning the potential of US health care. The right-wing think-tanks in the late 1980s made a big effort to boost the image of US health care, while sometimes admitting that it was the potential of new competitive trends in the US rather than the reality of the system that was impressive. But disillusionment with the market in US health care was quick to set in, as in the 1960s.

Now the need for stronger planning and governmental setting of priorities is on the agenda in the US. Bush's government probably cannot deliver, given the fragmented structure of US government and lack of will in the executive, but at least the US is now kinder and gentler. For Bush after Reagan, read Major after Thatcher. The radical edge of the White Paper has had its day. The following characteristics of US health care suggest why. It hitched its prospects for success to the wrong ideological chariot.

ANALYSIS OF US HEALTH CARE INTO THE 1990s

The US is well known for medical innovation and high-quality care in certain high-technology specialties. The health care system is, however, in crisis. Health care absorbs about 12% of the GDP, and costs are rising at continuously high rates despite cost control measures adopted throughout the 1970s and 1980s. The US spends approximately $2,200 per capita per annum on health care. On the other hand, there is more inequity and lack of access in US health care than in any other advanced, Western country. There are approximately 40 million uninsured, and inequality in access to health care by those who need it is marked. The combination of costs which are out of control and inequity is a depressing one for most Americans.

What are the reasons for this situation? Political reasons are dominant. In most of Europe, national health insurance schemes cover all citizens, and their contributions to such schemes are linked to ability to pay. In the US, there is no national scheme, reflecting both political individualism and the difficulty the political system has in passing comprehensive social legislation. In the US, private insurance, like all commercial insurance, reflects risk. In consequence, the poorer and the sicker in society face difficulty in finding access to affordable insurance. The mainstream US citizen is covered by either his/her own private insurance, or more likely, employer-provided insurance. On changing job, this insurance may not continue and the fragmented system is both inequitable and inefficient. Government programmes, primarily Medicare for the elderly and Medicaid for certain categories of the poor, are also in financial difficulties because of the massive budget deficit.

Added to fragmentation in financing, fragmentation in provision of care causes an inability to control costs. Under third-party insurance, neither the doctor, the hospital, nor the consumer/patient has a direct incentive to limit the costs of treatment. The third-party payer is often faced, therefore, with spiralling costs. The most prominent attempt to change this perverse incentive has been through the development of HMOs. A characteristic of an HMO is that a consumer pays an annual premium to what is a special type of insurance company, which also employs or directly contracts with the providers of health care (doctors, hospitals, and other health-care institutions). In consequence, the providers' profligacy is directly registered in diminished profits, if the HMO is for-profit, or surplus, if the HMO is non-profit, of the institution as a whole. However, HMOs, although spreading, still account for only about 15% of US health care.

Adding to the extremely poor cost-effectiveness of American health care are the extremely high administrative costs which are necessary to police, regulate, and run such a fragmented and already expensive system. In Canada and Europe, there is not a plethora of competing health insurance plans or competing providers. In a system such as Britain's NHS, there is the potential for even more administrative economy. However, in the US, most private insurance is provided by particular employers. A major source of inequity, especially for the unemployed in an increasingly depressed economy, is compounded by a major source of administrative complexity.

There have been attempts to control costs in the 1970s and 1980s. In the 1970s, the more old-fashioned systems for reimbursing hospitals, such as regulation of the per diem reimbursement, came under regulatory control. For both political and economic reasons these were not successful: they tended to be subverted politically and were of limited effect in that the basic incentive for hospitals, to keep patients in as long as possible, still remained. Newer systems, such as reimbursement of hospitals by DRGs, have had more success than measures in the 1970s.

DRGs are not generalized throughout the system, as it is only the federal government's payments under the Medicare programme which are regulated according to the DRG system. However, there have been attempts to copy the system in the private sector. Essentially, a DRG pertains to a medical condition and covers patients whose illnesses are similar and whose need for service or demands upon the system can be considered to be similar. An expected costing is then derived from such a procedure, which is used for reimbursement. Costs may be considered to be controlled better in that there is incentive for hospitals to promote shorter length of stay, or perhaps day-care treatment, in order to minimize costs which are not reimbursed per diem any longer.

Whereas the old system encouraged longer length of stay, the new system encourages more admissions, and indeed early discharge and readmissions. Furthermore, physicians have become adept at redesignating patients from a DRG which does not pay much to a DRG which pays more! Thus, this policy also has had a limited effect upon the control of costs, as well as worrying effects such as discharge which is too early.

There is greater competition in provision throughout the health-care system. Attempts to limit the number of facilities through the planning system had been promulgated in the 1970s. This was based on the theory that supply creates its own demand in health care, as in other areas of life, and that therefore limiting facilities and expansion of facilities could limit total costs to be reimbursed. However, political factors interfered with the policy of the so-called planning, which was in fact a crude form of capital planning, was in fact a very weak, timid, and eventually discarded form of regulation. Especially after Ronald Reagan's victory in the presidential election of 1980, there was a move to promote competition as the answer to greater efficiency, rather than planning, in the provision of health care. However, this has also had a limited effect. Admittedly, there has been such a great expansion of the US post-war health economy that, at the margin, some providers have surplus beds and facilities and are therefore susceptible to tighter conditions by purchasers of health care. Overall, however, competition is not active enough to control costs.

Unfortunately, increasingly regulated forms of reimbursement, while unsuccessful in controlling costs in the aggregate, are making it less possible for hospitals to cross-subsidize care for the uninsured and poor out of the surplus income from caring for richer or well-insured patients. In consequence, social problems resulting from lack of access to health care by the poor are worsening, not improving.

It would make sense for the US to copy European systems such as the Dutch or even German system, whereby regionalized and powerful purchasers of health care, such as sick funds and insurance companies, would have more muscle in controlling profligate providers. In Britain, total spending on health care is rigidly controlled, and the district health authority, the only real purchaser of muscle, can dictate terms to providers very effectively, even after the recent changes to increase market forces in the provision of health care. European systems allow equity, as premiums are related to individual means. They also encourage efficiency through controlling costs at the aggregate level, and, due to recent reforms in countries such as Holland, such systems are capable of incorporating competitive mechanisms in provision without recourse to the anarchy of the US health market.

In practice, however, again for political reasons, it is unlikely that the US will go down this road. With the rise and fall of both for-profit health care and what now seem Utopian competitive solutions to health-care problems, the only possible route for the US is through greater regulation of both providers and insurers. This could be coupled with the federal government expanding the Medicaid programme to include those currently uninsured. Enthoven, a leading health economist identified with reform both in the US and now in Britain, has argued that this could be done without significant cost to the Treasury, for the reason that the whole Medicaid programme currently costs less than tax allowances for private health care. If these were controlled such that only affordable and efficient health insurance was tax deductible, there would be a large amount of tax money available for the federal government to spend.

There are embryonic signs as we move into the 1990s that Congress will go down the road of more rather than less regulation. Congress has already authorized the development of a Resource Based Relative Values Scale (RBRVS) on which a fee schedule for Medicare should be based, which for the first time controls physicians' own costs and gives a greater bias to primary care. However, it is early days, as with all other attempts at reform since the 1970s, to conclude that in such a development lies an effective future health care system!

The US's health-care system has been studied in many European countries which are moving towards privatization in health care in one form or another. However, the US private system contains more negative lessons than positive ones. There is simply not the central control to promote hospital and physician behaviour consistent with the country's health objectives. Capital-investment decisions are taken at such a decentralized level that even private institutions cannot control them. Running costs continue to be out of control. Inequity in access to health care is worsening, not improving. There is a need for strategic regulation, compatible with the private market in order to fulfil US policy-makers' wishes, to improve matters in the US health-care system. President Bush's weak exhortation to private initiative is simply not enough.

National health insurance is again nominally on the agenda, but it is unlikely to be implemented in any meaningful form – as in the late 1960s and early 1970s, when times were more propitious. Admittedly, the economic crisis at the beginning of the 1990s has led to greater generosity in funding Medicaid, reversing the Reagan cuts to some extent, but this is not yet even a straw in the wind.

BRITISH HEALTH CARE AFTER THE WHITE PAPER

In Britain, the political impetus behind the White Paper, which is fundamentally Thatcherite and pro-US, has quickly been lost. The early 1990s show a trend back to planned and managed health care, which is good news for defenders of the NHS.

Conservative policy is no longer geared to 'tackling' the NHS as the next public sector target, as would have been very likely in a fourth Conservative term with Mrs Thatcher as Prime Minister. On the other hand, Conservative policy is to extend 'self-governing trusts' and GP fund-holding practices, which both diminish the capacity for needs-based planning by district population and increase problems of co-ordinating provision with financing.

Maintaining co-ordinated delivery of care in such an environment necessitates that health authorities, Family Health Service Authorities and GP practices agree on priorities and on the services to be purchased for patients – whether in a primary setting or as a result of patients referrals. Thus, planning is even more bureaucratic and 'costly' than before. Purchaser–provider separation, in such a scenario, is in effect an obstacle to be overcome by regulation and 'joint planning', not a market-oriented liberation.

After the Labour and Conservative Party Conferences of 1991, health was even more of a political issue than it had been in the spring, when inequity arising from GP fundholding behaviour had hit the headlines.

Firstly, the chief executive of the NHS management executive, Mr Duncan Nichol entered the political debate by denying Labour's accusation that the Conservatives wanted to privatize the NHS. This was unorthodox behaviour. Mr Nichol already knew he would be replaced, in all probability, by a Labour government, as he had nailed his colours strongly to the Kenneth Clarke mast earlier in the 1980s. So he had nothing to lose. Moreover, he was probably seeking to tease out more unequivocal denials of intent to privatize from his political bosses, as he opposed privatization himself. Nevertheless, the move backfired, as it was seen as lacking in propriety; Robin Cook, the shadow Secretary of State for Health, referred Mr Nichol's remarks to the Cabinet Secretary.

Secondly, and more significantly, Labour made headway by persuading almost 70% of the public that the Conservatives might privatize the NHS. When asked to justify the charge, Labour politicians pointed out that care was increasingly rationed, i.e. that certain procedures would now require private finance, if refused on the NHS either nationally or by a local purchasing health authority; that trusts could easily be privatized thereby privatizing provision; and that general underfunding encouraged the private sector's growth. Although the money followed the patient in the post-White-Paper NHS, there was not enough money to fund all referrals. As a result, hospitals were often in cash crises, just like in the pre-White-Paper NHS, if they treated such patients.

The pricing system in the new market NHS encouraged price discrimination. As a result, discrepancies existed – certain patients were more attractive than others to providers. Coupled with local purchasers' different priorities, the care to which one was entitled might now depend on where one lived. In the pre-White-Paper NHS, the resource-allocation formula had often given districts (then providers as well as purchasers) an incentive to discriminate between residents of the district and non-residents. The White Paper, by giving to districts budgets only for their residents, was supposed to end this. Yet in practice price discrimination accentuated discrepancies.

Thirdly, Labour's own policy for the 1990s came into the spotlight. The policy was to bring trusts back into direct health authority control.

Nevertheless, Labour would still seek to separate health authority functions between strategy set by a strategic board and provision run by an operational board. Flexi-funding of health authorities was perhaps the most interesting and controversial proposal. It was argued by some commentators that extra cash for hospitals which out-performed targets could lead either to holding back money from other purposes or to a continuing spiral of extra money which would in effect break cash limits. What these commentators did not point out was that such extra funding would be the mechanism whereby controlled additional NHS spending was furnished. Admittedly, targets would have to be carefully devised, to prevent phoney achievement or denial of bonuses to good performers who somehow missed targets.

What such commentators did not make clear, also, was the fact that funding efficient and effective providers better could be financed by planned closures and reallocations. Naturally, Labour did not highlight such necessities – no party would. But the essence of Labour policy was to end the needless anarchy of a phoney market, and institute a planning system which nevertheless gave incentives to good provision.

Labour was agreeing not to dismantle new management arrangements, except for undemocratic health authorities themselves, increasingly ruled before 1992 by Conservative placemen as chairmen. In other words, proposals such as those from Labour-leaning Institute for Public Policy Research, to give all health responsibilities to the Department of the Environment were seen as unnecessarily disruptive. In return for pragmatism, Labour would expect co-operation from an NHS management cadre, which had naïvely accepted the purchaser–provider split as an inevitable trend, when in fact it caused problems abroad rather than resolved them. Meeting need necessitated planned provision, not a contracting rigmarole.

Labour's policy document, *Your Good Health* (Labour Party, 1992), promised to abolish the market in health care, while arguing for performance agreements, incentives, a quality commission and a 'trouble shooter' for problems to address the questions of better outcomes and better management. Health authorities would have responsibility for an integrated strategy for primary and secondary care, and would reflect, in part, local populations' priorities. People treated outside their district would be accounted for without the bureaucracy of either the White Paper or the predecessor arrangements.

Abolishing the institutionalized purchaser–provider split was the most controversial proposal, and ending GP fundholding also created argument. GPs had been given a politically-motivated incentive to 'opt-out' (as had trusts) in that if they did not hold their own funds, they would face increasingly bureaucratic negotiations with purchasing districts. Labour argued that it was better to allow all GPs to have an input into determining needs. It can be added here that the Conservatives were encouraging such joint planning also, but by a bureaucratic back door. After the White Paper, FHSAs have been confused as to their role; Labour would integrate   them into local health authorities. These, in turn, would have overall responsibility for both planning and provision. Was it really impossible for providing managers to be allowed a say as to priorities at the general level? After all, clinical directors within providers are allowed a say as to overall hospital priorities.

Gaining the theoretical benefits of a purchaser–provider split overall necessitated ending an anarchic split in practice, argued Labour. If a split allowed longer-term or new priorities to be addressed, why had the opposite occurred – in a welter of short-termism, haggles over contracts and a quantity obsession at the expense of outcomes.

By the general election, the two parties had some implicit themes in common, but distinct stances on a number of important matters.

References

Alford, R.R. (1975) *Health Care Politics: Ideological and Interest-Group Barriers to Reform*, Univ. Chicago Press, Chicago.

Audit Commission (1986) *Making a Reality of Community Care*, HMSO, London.

Bevan, G., Holland, W., Maynard, A., and Mays, N. (1988) *Reforming UK Health Care To Improve Health: The Case for Research and Experiment*, United Medical and Dental Schools, and Centre for Health Economics, Univ. York, and UMDS, London.

Black, Sir Douglas (1980) *Inequalities in Health*, HMSO, London.

British Medical Association (1988) 'Evidence to the government internal review of the National Health Service', *British Medical J.* (296) pp. 1411–8.

British Medical Association (1989) *Special Report on the Government's White Paper, Working for Patients*, BMA, London.

Brittan, L. (1988) *A New Deal for Health Care*, Conservative Political Centre, London.

Butler, F. and Pirie, M. (1988) *The Health of Nations*, Adam Smith Instit., London.

Dekker (1987) (Commissie Struktuur en Financiering) Bereidheid tot veraiderung Gravenhage: Staatsdrukkerij.

DHSS (1976a) *Priorities for Health and Personal Social Services*, HMSO, London.

DHSS (1976b) *Sharing Resources for Health in England* (The RAWP Report) HMSO, London.

DHSS (1977) *The Way Forward*, HMSO, London.

DHSS (1981) *Patients First*, HMSO, London.

DHSS (1981) *Care in the community*, HMSO, London.

DHSS (1981) *Care in Action*, HMSO, London.

DoH (1989a) *Working for Patients* (White Paper) Cmnd. 555, HMSO, London.

DoH (1989b) *Working Papers 1–8* (White Paper) HMSO, London.

DoH (1989c) *Caring for People* (White Paper) HMSO, London

DoH (1991) *The Health of the Nation*, HMSO, London.

Enthoven, A.C. (1985) *Reflections on the Management of the National Health Service*, Nuffield Prov. Hosp. Trust, London.

Enthoven, A.C. (1988) *The Theory and Practice of Managed Competition*, Elsevier, Amsterdam.

Field, F. (1988) various newspaper reports.

Green, D. (1986) *Challenge to the NHS*. Instit. Economic Affairs, London.

Green, D. (1988) *Everyone a Private Patient* Instit. Economic Affairs Health Unit, London.

Griffiths, E.R. (1983) *Letter to the Secretary of State* (The Griffiths Inquiry Report) DHSS, London.

Griffiths, E.R. (1988) *Community Care: Agenda for Action*, HMSO, London.

Ham, C. (1985) *Health Policy in Britain*, 2nd edn, Macmillan, Studies in Social Policy, London.

Klein, R. (1989) *The Politics of the National Health Service*, 2nd edn, Longmans, London.

The Labour Party (1990) *A Fresh Start for Health*, Labour Party, Walworth Rd, London.

The Labour Party (1992) *Your Good Health*, Labour Party, Walworth Rd, London.

McLachlan, G. and Maynard, A. (1982) *The Public/Private Mix for Health: Relevance and Effects of Change*, Nuffield Prov. Hosp. Trust, London.

McLachlan, G. (1990) *What Price Quality?* (Rock Carling Lecture), Nuffield Prov. Hosp. Trust, London.

MORI/Nuffield Prov. Hosp. Trust (1985) *A Review of Surveys Conducted about the NHS* (unpub.).

NHS Management Board (1988) *Review of the Resource Allocation Working Party Formula* (final report), HMSO, London.

NHS Management Executive (1990) *Contracts for Health Services: Operating Contracts*, HMSO, London.

Nordlinger, E. (1981) *On the Autonomy of the Democratic State*, Harvard Univ. Press, Cambridge, MA.

Owen, D. (1985) Keynote Address, Instit. Health Services Management Annual Conference, Coventry (June).

Paton, C. (1988) 'Trouble with the health maintenance organization', *British Medical J.* (297) pp. 934–5.

Paton, C. (1990) *US Health Politics: Public Policy and Political Theory*, Gower, Aldershot.

Redwood, J. (1988) *In Sickness and in Health: Managing Change in the NHS*, Centre for Policy Studies, London.

Redwood, J. and Letwin, O.(1988) *Britain's Biggest Enterprise: Ideas for Radical Reforms of the NHS*, London, Centre for Policy Studies, London.

Starr, P. (1983) *The Social Transformation of American Medicine*, Harvard Univ. Press, Cambridge, MA.

Stowe, (Sir) K., (1988) *On Caring For the National Health*, Nuffield Prov. Hosp. Trust, London.

Taylor-Gooby, P. (1985) *Public Opinion, Ideology, and State Welfare*, Routledge & Kegan Paul, London.

Townsend, P., Phillimore, P. and Beattie, A. (1988) *Health and Deprivation*, Croom Helm, London.

Whitehead, M. (1987) *The Health Divide*, Health Education Council, London.

Willetts, D. (1987) 'The role of the Prime Minister's policy unit', *Public Administration* (65) 4, pp. 443–54.

Willetts, D. and Goldsmith, M. (1988) *Managed Health Care: A New System for a Better Health Service*, Centre for Policy Studies, London.

Further reading

Anonymous Editorial (1988) 'Another shock to the system for the NHS', *The Lancet*, 30 July 1988, pp. 260–1.

Bevan, G. and Spencer, A.H. (1984) 'Models of resource policy of health authorities, in *London Papers in Reginal Studies*, No. 13, *Planning and Analysis in Health Care Systems*, (ed. M. Clarke) Pion, London.

Bevan, G. (1989) 'Reforming UK health care; internal markets or emergent planning', *Fiscal Studies*, (10) 1 pp. 53–71.

Bevan, G. and Marinker, M. (1989) *Greening the White Paper: A Strategy for NHS Reform*, Social Market Foundation, London.

Black, Sir Douglas (1984) An Anthology of False Antitheses, Rock Carling Lecture, Nuffield Provincial Hospitals Trust, London.

Bosanquet, N. (1980) 'GPs as firms: creating an internal market for primary care', *Public Money*, March.

Centre for Disease Control (1986) 'Premature mortality in the US: public health issues in the use of years of potential life loss', *Mortality and Morbidity Weekly Report*, 35(25): supplement.

Committee of Inquiry into the Future Development of the Public Health Function (The Acheson Committee) (1988) *Public Health in England*, HMSO, London.

DHSS Forrest Committee (1986) *Breast Cancer Screening*, HMSO, London.

DHSS (1987) *Objectives of the Breast Cancer Screening Programme*, Regional Representatives' Meeting (July) HMSO, London.

Enthoven, A.C. (1989) 'A consumer choice health plan for the 1990s, universal health insurance. . . . ', Parts 1 & 2, *New England J. of Medicine*. (320) 1, 2, pp. 29–37; 94–101.

Green, D. (1988) (ed.) *Acceptable Inequalities: Essays on the Pursuit of Equality in Health Care*, Instit. Economic Affairs Health Unit, London.

Holland, W. (ed.) (1988) *European Community Atlas of Avoidable Death*, Oxford Univ. Press, Oxford, NY.

House of Commons Social Services Committee (1989) *Resourcing the National Health Service: The Government's Plans for the Future of the National Health Service*, eighth report, session 1988–89, HMSO, London.

House of Commons (1989) *National Health Service and Community Care Bill*, HMSO, London.

Jarman, B. (1985) 'Underprivileged Areas', in *The Medical Annual*, (ed D.J. Pereira Gray) pp. 224–43, Wright, Bristol.

Jennett, B. (1985) *High Technology Medicine*, Nuffield Prov. Hosp. Trust, London.

Kirkman-Liff, B.L., Lapre, R. and Kirkman-Liff, T.L. (1988) 'The metamorphosis of health planning in the Netherlands and the USA' *International J. of Health Planning and Management*, (3) 2, John Wiley & Sons, Chichester.

McCarthy, M. (1986) editorial, *British Medical J.* (292).

McLachlan, G. (1988) letters, *The Times*, 22 Feb.

Mayhew, L. (1986) *Urban Hospital Location*, George Allen & Unwin, London.

Mays, N. and Bevan, G. (1987) *Resource Allocation in the Health Service*, Bedford Square Press NCVO, London.

OECD (1987) *OECD Economic Studies*, OECD, Paris.

OECD (1987) *Financing and Delivering Health Care. A Comparative Analysis of OECD Countries*, Social Policy Studies No. 4, OECD, Paris.

OECD (1990), *Health Care Systems in Transition. The Search for Efficiency*, Organisation of Economic Cooperation and Development, Paris.

Paton, C. (1985) *The Policy of Resource Allocation and its Ramifications*, Nuffield Prov. Hosp. Trust, London.

Paton, C. (1989) 'Perestroika in the USSR health care system', *British Medical J.* (June).

Peet, J.(1987) *Healthy Competition*, Centre for Policy Studies (CPS), London.

Peters, T. and Waterman, R. (1982) *In Search of Excellence*, Macmillan, London.

Peters, T. (1987) *Thriving on Chaos*, Macmillan, London.

Ranade, W. (1989) *To market, to market*, Nat. Assoc. Health Authorities (NAHA), Birmingham.

Richmond, J.B. and Kotelchuk, M. (1990) 'Co-ordination and development of strategies and policy for public health in the United States', *Oxford Textbook of Public Health*, 2nd edn, Oxford Univ. Press, Oxford.

Robinson, R. (1988) *Efficiency and the NHS: A Case for Internal Markets*, Instit. Econ. Affairs Health Unit Paper No. 2, IEA, London.

Royal College of General Practitioners (1985) *Quality and General Practice*, RCGP, London.

Scheffler, R.M. and Rossiter, L.F. (eds) (1988) *Advances in Health Economics and Health Services Research Volume 9: Private Sector Involvement in Health Care: Implications for Access, Cost and Quality*, Part III, 'Health Care Coalitions: Community and Change'.

Secretaries of State for Social Services, Wales, Northern Ireland and Scotland (1986) *Primary Health Care: An Agenda for Discussion*, HMSO, London.

Whitney, R. (1988) *National Health Crisis: A Modern Solution*, Shepheard-Walwyn, London.

Willetts, D. (1988) 'Address', *Financial Times* Conference on Private Health Care, London. (unpublished)

World Health Organization (1989) *World Health Statistics Quarterly*, (42) 1, 'Preventable mortality', pp. 4–10, WHO, Geneva.

World Health Organization, Regional Office for Europe (Hospital Programme) (1989), *An Analysis of the Support of First Referral Hospitals to PHC Services in the UK*, Copenhagen.

Index